THE

C000283242

THE BLITZ
Westminster at War

WILLIAM SANSOM

OXFORD UNIVERSITY PRESS
1990

Oxford University Press, Walton Street, Oxford OX2 6DP

Oxford New York Toronto
Delhi Bombay Calcutta Madras Karachi
Petaling Jaya Singapore Hong Kong Tokyo
Nairobi Dar es Salaam Cape Town
Melbourne Auckland

and associated companies in
Berlin Ibadan

Oxford is a trade mark of Oxford University Press

First published 1947 by Faber and Faber
First issued as an Oxford University Press paperback 1990

British Library Cataloguing in Publication Data
Sansom, William, 1912–1976
[Westminster in war] The Blitz : Westminster at war.
1. London. (London Borough) Westminster. Air raids,
1939–1945, by Germany, Luftwaffe
I. [Westminster in war] II. Title
III. Sansom, William, 1912–1976. Wall
940.54212132
ISBN 0-19-285218-3

Printed in Great Britain by
Clays Ltd.
Bungay, Suffolk

FOREWORD
by Stephen Spender

This book provides a complete account of Civil Defence during World War II in the City of Westminster, a part of London which includes Westminster Abbey, the Houses of Parliament, Buckingham Palace, Belgravia, Soho, Oxford Street—Sansom gives a full description of what might today be described as prime 'Tourists' London' in his Introduction.

William Sansom was not a historian but a novelist and short story writer of remarkable quality: yet *The Blitz* provides a model for the historian in the picture it gives of the formation, structure and performance of Civil Defence together with description of the personnel— firemen, air raid wardens, ambulance workers, doctors, nurses, rescue teams, etc., 'on the job'.

First published in 1947 with full co-operation from the Home Office, *The Blitz* (first titled *Westminster in War*) counts, I suppose, as an officially sponsored publication yet there is nothing that seems official and stuffy about it. However statistical and barely factual the information conveyed in describing the elaborate structure of Civil Defence, Sansom seems always to swim—efficiently, briskly and even humorously—above the surface of all this material.

True, there is nothing here about firemen occasionally looting on the fires which they heroically quenched; and very little about day to day life on the stations of air raid wardens, firemen and ambulance crews at times when these men and women were not actually dealing with raids. Yet Sansom achieves the extraordinary in managing to make his narrative personal, while keeping it completely anonymous as regards those involved in the actions portrayed. Nor is his book in the slightest degree egoistical: one does not grasp here that throughout the war Sansom was himself a London fireman, the author remains as anonymous as the cast involved in the many dramas of Blitz, post-Blitz and pilotless raids which—with a vivid sense of drama—he describes. It is, as I shall show later, from his fiction that one gets the feel of his own autobiography during war.

The reader may regret the anonymity—the lack of names and descriptions—illustrations like newspaper photographs attached to actions. Yet it is an important part of Sansom's achievement that he *can* make a virtue of the anonymity which he sets up as a matter of principle here. As he explains in his Introduction:

Courage is a matter of individual resource, of personal make-up and personal will. It is impossible to generalise, all arguments are here invidious. And so particularly for this reason no names at all are to be mentioned in this record, no assessments of personal enterprise or discretion. Individual actions will be described, and single achievements—but it is the intent to record these as part and indicative of the whole rather than as episodes personally significant; they are types of episode, many truly courageous, many truly examples of endurance, but to be matched always against the other quieter courages, unseen and unrecorded, which must have gone to the making of an unbroken line.

The attitude of the writer here seems close to that of the painter and friend of painters (Leonard Rosamon was on the same fire station as Sansom). And one can easily imagine the writer of this book being a painter of the Blitz. Apart from certain photographs of the results of bombardment—some of them reproduced here—there are no works of art from which we derive a greater impression of London under bombardment than Henry Moore's Shelter drawings of Londoners taking shelter during the Blitz on the platforms of London's Underground. The great sculptor's drawings of figures seated or lying down in these improvised shelters seem hewn out of the People's patience and endurance.

Like Henry Moore's drawings, William Sansom's word-sketches of Londoners in situations of bombardment have the power of their anonymity. What is particularly striking here is the vivid spontaneity with which images flash out of what may be factual information about the damage to lives and buildings caused by a raid, or about the number of engines called in to deal with what the log book in the fire station will have recorded as an 'incident'.

Here, for example, Sansom records an incident which, as he puts it, 'requires note':

An exploded and an unexploded bomb fell at the junction of Denbigh Street and Belgrave Road. The damage done was not unusual for such nights. Similar bombs had fallen without number in those first weeks. As it was, people were reported trapped in a vault shelter beneath the pavement. Water was pouring in from broken mains. It was feared that all those trapped would be drowned. Rescue work was made doubly dangerous by the discovery of a second unexploded bomb lying close by. To complicate matters, a gas main had been set alight. Gas engineers were called. The Auxiliary Fire Service were summoned both to restrict the fire and pump water out of the flooded basements beneath. Under those conditions, and always with the menace of further bombs overhead, rescue work went on through the night. Bodies were recovered from the water. It was found later that they had not been drowned, they were killed by the bomb.

FOREWORD

This is a straightforward account of an 'incident'. It might, one thinks, almost have been copied down with little alteration from material supplied to him by the authorities. But at this point the narrative broadens out into feeling and judgement much more personal:

Then, at a quarter to nine the next morning, the officer in charge of Westminster stretcher parties went over to inspect the gas-filled crater of the bomb diagnosed as unexploded. At that moment it exploded. The officer received injuries to his head from which he died.

This man died in an attempt to save others. His death stands as a monument not only to his own courage but to the sacrifice of all those who undertook the dangerous task of identifying those bombs of delayed action, and who were themselves no less courageous—perhaps just luckier.

While singling out the courage of this particular officer, Sansom gives his courage the characteristic of anonymity as though courage were something the courageous themselves did not know they had until circumstances produced the situation in which—perhaps to their own surprise—they discovered it in themselves. Courage, he seems to suggest, was a quality of the Service of which individual acts of bravery were the symptoms.

I wrote above that the incident described here read almost like an official account of what happened at the corner where Denbigh Street and Belgrave Road meet. But the events described exactly in the order or sequence in which they happened has something of early Hemingway about it: when Hemingway would follow in the description on the printed page the exact sequence of events imagined or described as happening in reality.

In his second chapter, Sansom describes how Civilian Defence came into being, through the co-operation of the city planners (Westminster being one of the most advanced) with the team at the Home Office. Given the fact that the planners of Civil Defence had no experience of the conditions of modern warfare waged against civilians to work on (apart perhaps from the small scale bombings by the Luftwaffe on Madrid and Barcelona during the Spanish Civil War) they showed remarkable foresight. One may pause to marvel that the will of the planners was not paralysed by thinking of the conditions anticipated. (As planners today seem paralysed by the thought of nuclear war.) For the fact is that in the late Thirties the prospect of London being bombed by the Luftwaffe with bombs incomparably more effective than those dropped on London in World War I seemed almost as terrifying in anticipation as, in the event, the bombing of Hiroshima proved to be. It was commonplace at that time to say that the next war would be the end of civilization. At the time of Munich, when Londoners dug trenches for shelters in Hyde Park and when there was no anti-aircraft artillery, it seemed that London would be defencelessly exposed to aerial attack by a totalitarian enemy capable of totally destroying it. The vision of World War II was, before it happened, apocalyptic, and indeed it did come to provide glimpses of apocalypse.

Sansom skilfully makes his account of the forming of the various services of Civil Defence a kind of skeletal structure which he fleshes with the lives of people in those services and with Londoners who were not in them.

In his chapter 'After the Raid', as well as describing rescue and clearance operations, he brilliantly portrays the continuity of London life throughout the Blitz; how people carried on living comparatively normal lives during these years. He notes that during the far less terrifying period of the Little Blitz morale was at a lower ebb than during the Blitz, partly as the result of the nervously exhausting effect of two years of war, and, one might add, of one year almost without bombardment. He notes how in 1945 the effect of the pilotless—V1 and V2—raids was exhausting to a degree where, had they continued, there might have been real demoralisation.

*

Sansom is one of those writers whose writing seems very close to their way of talking. In his case, I would describe this as fully informed, while given both to flashes of humour and outbursts expressing formidably held opinions; also branching out into virtuoso passages of illustration. In *The Blitz*, while always conscious of the densely informative requirements of his assignment, he is never swamped by the factual. His writing maintains always the quality of highly civilized and agreeable conversation.

I have mentioned the possible influence of Hemingway in the ordering of his narrative but the influences which really fire him in his fiction—and which sometimes do even here—are Kafkaesque and surrealist. Kafka was of course fascinated by the mysterious role played in people's lives by the bureaucracy of the Austrian Empire. Similarly, the complexity of the organization of Civil Defence had a certain fascination for William Sansom here; just as the 'incidents'—air raids— often appealed to the surrealist in him—as his fiction about fire-fighting shows.

The first work I ever read by him was a short story called 'The Long Sheet', submitted to *Horizon* when I was assisting Cyril Connolly in editing that magazine. This was a Kafkaesque account of a group of prisoners whose punishment was, under the supervision of warders, to wring bone-dry—absolutely purged of the last drop of moisture—a long wet sheet. The story showed Sansom's fascination with the execution and minutiae of organized procedures, the commedia of their structures and rules as they affect people's lives.

Throughout the war Sansom was, as I have noted, a fireman in London. Some stories he wrote which are influenced by his experiences of fire-fighting, reveal his fascination with what was often a surreal experience. For Sansom, the spectacular fire is seen here as an almost privileged entry into an elemental world of a reality completely different from everything outside it, with laws of its own which involve the suspension of all the maps and time-tables of the world.

In the story 'The Wall' the fireman-narrator, standing surrounded by fire at the centre of a blazing building, sees in the space of what is for him an enormously expanded time a wall collapse onto him and two fellow firemen:

The second was timeless. I had leisure to remark many things. For instance that an iron derrick, slightly to the left, would not hit me. This derrick stuck out from the building and I could feel its sharpness and hardness as clearly as if I had run my body intimately over its contours. I had time to notice that it carried a footlong hook, a chain with three-inch rings, two girder supports and a wheel more than twice as large as my head.

A wall will fall in many ways. It may sway over to the one side or the other. It may crumble at the very beginning of its fall. It may remain intact and fall flat. This wall fell flat as a pancake. It clung to its shape through ninety degrees to the horizontal. Then it detached itself from the pivot and fell down on top of us.

The last resistance of bricks and mortar at the pivot point cracked off like automatic gun-fire. The violent sound both deafened us and brought us to our senses. We dropped the hose and crouched. Afterwards Verno said that I knelt slowly on one knee with bowed head, like a man about to be knighted. Well, I got my knighting. There was an incredible noise—a thunderclap condensed into the space of an eardrum—and then the bricks and the mortar came tearing and burning into the flesh of my face.

In a passage such as this it is difficult to discern the boundary between the fantastic and the real—if there is such a boundary. Indeed there seems to be some collusion between the two, real and the fantastic, which weaves fantasy out of reality. The peculiar gift of William Sansom was to observe this fusion with hawk's eye attention and to record it with the utmost precision. The passion for observation and the delight in the peculiar are what give his writing its élan: as though the Blitz were the producer of tragic jokes which amused and even at times delighted him but which he wrote down with detached consciencious-ness.

In one story, 'Fireman Flower', Sansom explores the possibilities of surrealist fantasy offered by fires which destroyed warehouses at the London docks in the autumn of 1940. Given the contents of these warehouses, firemen were sometimes to find themselves knee deep in waves of boiling tea, or liquid sugar, or in pools of whisky or wine, or having their eyes stung with burning pepper. Sansom was in his amusedly serious way fascinated by the priestly injunction of the officers of the Fire Service to their men to 'get to the centre of the fire!' For him this had something ritualistic, primevally sacrificial about it. The story begins with Fireman Flower in the van where with his fellow firemen he is riding to what all know to be 'an important fire', reflecting:

My task is succinctly to discover the kernel of the fire. I must disregard the fire's offshoots, I must pass over the fire's deceptive encroachments, and I must proceed most determinedly in search of the fire's kernel.

In 'Fireman Flower' Sansom draws on the experience of fire-fighting in the earliest phase of the Blitz when the Luftwaffe attacked the London docks. Firemen had, in these fires, as I wrote above, the experience of being literally overwhelmed or drenched by falling objects spilled onto them from containers. In 'Fireman Flower' these are exotically intoxicating. In their penetration of the kernel of the fire, Fireman Flower finds himself in a long low room where the heat has melted bottles of scent:

He thought ... perfumed gas? His brain pumped madly against the odorous blow. Smell pounded through his arteries, whirling his equilibrium, blinding him to all direction. Yet even in that first moment his senses thrummed alive with a great ecstasy—for this was an immense and wonderful perfume that drowned the air. Perfume that came not from one bottle, but from hundreds of little glinting bottles that had been burst by the fire and were now throwing out swiftly the vapour of their hot essences. Flower tried to think—'This is a fire. I have been to fires and I know that the world is somersaulted at a fire. Everything can happen. The ground may swill with moulten rubber so that firemen are stuck like flies on fly-paper. Dead grain married to hosewater may live again and move—the little wheat sperms may bring huge buildings crashing down around them. Towering walls move silently towards you, animated in the tall night sky.

The firemen become intoxicated by the scented alcohol. At the centre of such a blaze—the kernel—enter a kind of stillness, if not of silence, that of another world where, screened off by flames or red-hot wood, or brick, or iron, you feel yourself at the centre of a forest, of the universe where time and place are different from time and place outside. It is the world of Joseph Conrad's eye of the storm where real things behave as though they were activated by pure imagination.

After *Horizon* accepted 'The Long Sheet' in late 1940 I met William Sansom who persuaded me that when I was called up, later that year, I should join the Fire Service. This I did though I never took part in any of the really great fires of the Blitz, which stopped early in 1941 at the very moment almost when I had completed my training. As my wife and I lived in a kind of garret on top of a house in Maresfield Gardens I worked at the nearest station which was in that very road where William Sansom and the artist Leonard Rosamon were also firemen.

Extremely modest, Bill Sansom was not at all 'the writer'. In fact, I doubt whether any of his fellow firemen, apart from Lenny and I, knew that he wrote stories. He had an air of quiet efficiency, and everyone liked him. He had a great understanding of his fellow firemen. The nearest he got to literature when he and I talked together was in describing their characters, which he always discussed with sympathy. He did not regard them as 'amusing rogues' which was the attitude towards them of another writer, Henry Green, at a Kensington fire station.

Not, of course, that they were angels. I remember once in a dormitory of our fire station a discussion taking place in the darkness as to whether or not it was wrong to steal on a fire. There were in fact good enough reasons for thinking it was not very wrong, since, if not stolen, the loot would be destroyed, and anyway would never find its owner. Finally my fellow firemen decided that they did draw the line at stealing 'kids' cash boxes' . . . But this is to enter a world not touched on in *The Blitz*, though interesting.

Yet one never feels, reading this book, that any side of the life described has been left out. It is a work that so perfectly fulfils the terms of its assignment that its very limitations contribute to make it, within its terms, a work of art. And within those terms, it is a masterpiece.

CONTENTS

ILLUSTRATIONS

ACKNOWLEDGEMENTS

Plates 1 and 2 are supplied by courtesy of *THE TIMES*; Plate 7 a Ministry of Information photograph—Crown Copyright reserved.

INTRODUCTION

I t may be, with all that has been written of the recent German intrusion upon our cities, that the title of this record could be met with the hearty whisper: 'Why? Why on earth another book about it? And why on the precise earth of Westminster?'

There are reasons. It must be the first object of this foreword to introduce and define them. And to make a beginning it would be as well to rearrange a familiar concept—Westminster does not mean Whitehall. Whitehall is part of the City of Westminster, about a twentieth part, and the City proper extends far beyond. It radiates from the embankment by Whitehall like an immense and jagged fan as far east as the Temple and Fetter Lane; as far north as Oxford Street; as far west as the Broad Walk of Kensington Gardens, the Royal Albert Hall, and thence inwards again to Lowndes Street and the vicinity of Ranelagh Gardens to the River. Its southern boundary lies underwater, in mid-bed of the Thames, from Chelsea Bridge to the Temple Pier. The City area contains the districts of Soho, the West End, Mayfair, the Strand, Whitehall, Victoria, Belgravia, Pimlico and what is still described felicitously as the Hamlet of Knightsbridge. There is thus enclosed a various microcosm of famous and infamous London, of places of work and places of amusement, of the poorest residence and of the richest, of the palaces of Kings and Government and of the majority of those places of character and celebrity by which London is generally most known.

The first reason for this book, then, is to provide a record of the war years for the citizens of this City; and for its million visitors.

Secondly, it should tell the story in greater detail than has otherwise been possible of the bombardment and defence of celebrated buildings and well-known places, of an area that is the heart of London and has become so much a symbol of things English. It is not contended by any means that in human terms this City is more important than anywhere else. Obviously it is not. It just happens to be better known and to perform in its nature functions of national importance. Though its interest

9

extends beyond this—for there are involved here such varying strata of life, from the foreign elements of Soho to the working classes of Pimlico, from Mayfair's leisure to the great office districts and to the province of factories to the south that helps to make Westminster, surprisingly, the third largest industrial area in the County of London. This book should therefore record also an unusual fusion of diverse classes and interests in a combined citizen effort against the fiery gentlemen in grey.

There will be an opportunity, too, to experience here the general by way of the particular. Down-to-earth human experience can be conveyed with greater accuracy and more feeling where the field is limited, where there is time and space to deal with individual happenings, in detail, without the necessity to comprehend only the greater generalities. The field, though large, is boundaried. There will be time here to investigate square yards, minutes, single units of human experience; though much of necessity must be omitted, for there are almost six years to talk of and scarcely six miles of paper to deal with them. Much will have to be representative, typical, instant of the greater part. And here a word in deference to those anywhere in the City who have suffered— and find that in this history both the place and the time of their particular distress have been overstepped: *overstepped* must be the word in their ear, not overlooked, for some parallel experience will be found, at another date, in another street, on another page, that must stand as typical or symbolic of what was theirs.

Finally, this is the history of the efforts and achievements of a local government authority, of a Council. It is strange now to consider how before the war most people imagined themselves governed exclusively by a parliament sitting in that long spiky building by Big Ben, and paid no attention whatsoever to the amorphous fathers of the Town Hall, who, in many intimate matters unfettered by Whitehall, dealt with the most immediate necessities of life. Less than 40 per cent of Londoners troubled to vote at the last pre-war municipal elections. The Town Hall was thought of as a reliquary for countless clerks performing some perpetual and nameless task of a documentary nature, or as somewhere with steps down which the Mayor might walk before declaring into existence an Institute for Marine Biology, a Fire Station, an echelon of Brownies. As for the disappearance from the family bins of the family garbage—the Police or the Prime Minister himself might have sent along those angels with dusty trousers. A proportion of property-holders found their Council, after first ringing the Police, when they wanted perhaps a new bathroom; a proportion of labouring people knew of it, for it offered work; and otherwise a minority of the informed. But generally Local Government was unknown for what it really was, an intricate and executive organization that affected intimately the citizen's life—from the skilled surveying of new building developments to the collection of garbage (also skilled), from the erection of a lamp-post to the extermination of plague-rats, from the equipping of Libraries to the building of health centres for the very young. Broadly, the Council watches intimately over the welfare of its people; sees to it that conditions are right for the maximum general health, the maximum of ease and convenience on the public way; and devises much of the character and communal prosperity of its area. This is a big and a practical job. A Council is naturally staffed with architects, surveyors, doctors, lawyers and other skilled men. And so in wartime the responsibilities are immediately multiplied, its charge of the welfare of the people is instantly complicated with a host of new dangers. This book then will describe how one Council went to war: among the more resonant chords of destruction and death, of valorous action and strange endurance, there will be sung the unsung song of the clearing of streets, the billeting of the homeless, the provision of shelters, the building up of things torn down and the greater co-ordination of all other public services, of the unseen conduits of gas and water and electricity and the telephoned voice. It is hoped to present these functions as a picture rather than as a pyramid of figures, to exhibit a live impression of what went on behind the scenes and under the ground.

It has been said that the true character of war is not reflected in the battle so much as in the endurance and the ennui, the roughing and waiting, the long procession of small disgusts that dawdles intolerably before and after and in between battles. Intolerably—yet the marvel is its final toleration. It is true that under bombardment life in a city is physically more comfortable than in the field; but against this might be ranged a deeper mental discomfort, for the citizen lives still among familiar things, and over the threatened kitchen and the threatened shops there rests always the reminder of better days. These familiar places are much alienated and chilled in the shadow of war. They are emptied of people who made part of them and are filled with small signs—bready foods and dark curtains, steel helmets and sandbags, buckets and coupons; and on one night or other even this residue is smashed and burnt. There is felt always the impotence of not attacking, but being attacked. With this also the strange and sometimes absurd sensation of continuing in many cases without a uniform or any visible reassurance of duty, the phantom of a peacetime job in the grey-painted skeleton of a peacetime environment.

There are compensations. In war certain responsibilities are shrugged off or postponed. Others are assumed, but of a different, a more vivid, a shorter-lived nature. There are sensations of new virility, of paradoxical freedom, and of a rather bawdy 'live-for-to-day' philosophy. New tolerances are born between people; offsetting the paleness of worn nerves and the lining of sorrow there occurs a marvellous incidence of smiles where smiles have never been before: an unsettling vista of smiles, for one wondered how unsympathetic life could have been before, one was ashamed to reflect that it had needed a war to disinter the state of everyday comradeship. Under bombardment, people are conscious of a common cause, and since away in the future this has an object and an end, the spirit is energized and even curiously satisfied, for it likes things wrapped up in limits, with beginnings and ends; it can postpone the more unsettling questions of eternity and purpose.

However, these are compensations at a remove, and more memorable were the constant itches of daily frustration, and the fire and the terror by night. The battle itself brands the memory. And how then is courage to be assessed? When is most endured—in the long and patient years of working and watching, or in the shorter brilliancies of action? Phrases such as 'blind courage' are without meaning. For some there is an exhilaration to be found in the 'heat' of battle; on the other hand the man or woman who performs a dangerous and acrobatic rescue, or who fights a savage fire, or who sticks to a switchboard under concentrated bombing—all these may be frightened pale the whole time. Alternatively again, the switchboard worker may be phlegmatic, unmoved, and feel the whole of the time neither bored nor discomforted. Courage is a matter of individual resource, of personal make-up and personal will. It is impossible to generalize, all arguments are here invidious. And so particularly for this reason no names at all are to be mentioned in this record, no assessments of personal enterprise or discretion. Individual actions will be described, and single achievements —but it is the intent to record these as part and indicative of the whole rather than as episodes personally significant; they are types of episode, many truly courageous, many truly examples of endurance, but to be matched always against the other quieter courages, unseen and unrecorded, which must have gone to the making of an unbroken line.

In such a record as this, too, the curious and the freakish will tend to obtrude upon the more usual character of events, overpowering them. In the first days of bombing, for instance, one marvelled at pure debris;

but soon this became usual and to lift the human interest it took a bare tree gibbeted with hanging scarecrows from a blasted old-clothes shop, or an unbroken mirror hanging high-up on the façade of rooms disappeared. Rarities excite. Here they will be recorded and no doubt in their nature dominate the page; but one must try and recall always the tempestuous but humble greys that form their background, greys of great depth in whose neutrality lies the most profound history of how people lived and felt and loved and died. Even the freaks themselves outdo each other. In a while, as bombing continued, the unscathed mirror or picture hanging exposed on the wall became platitudinous—and it then took a row of ten grey Ascot toppers exposed in their open cupboard to raise the eyebrow. It was remarkable at first to find that as people were being unburied their first words often demanded neither safety nor life nor food—but their false teeth; however, in the hierarchy of events, even this curiosity of morale paled into nonentity on the night that one man was unburied and demanded from his rescuers, first and at all costs, his false nose.

Outstanding also will be the tale of various civic achievements, where Westminster instituted improvements ahead of the Government, which for various and more general high level reasons might have had to approach one matter or another with greater caution. For instance, Westminster bought on its own account and without guidance from above the first bunks to be used in shelters—12,000 of them several weeks before the Government took action; the City was first in providing lavatories and wash-places in shelters; and later in petitioning for the right to enrol women in fire-parties; and again in the enforcement of that legislation which compelled a private shelter to be opened to the public. These and others were achievements upon which the Council took an expensive but a necessary and successful chance. Again it would be well to remember that these are the figureheads to a vast amount of less dramatic achievement in the enormous and intricate and everyday task of running a city and providing for its citizens under attack from the air.

It devolves here to write only of the bombardment and the experience in war of Westminster—that is what the book is about. This will seem, from time to time, perhaps a little provincial. On some nights when Westminster suffered little, other parts of London underwent the most severe attack of the war. These tragedies often had their reaction in Westminster, for no part of London was properly divisible, geographically or sympathetically, from another. But for the purposes here a limit must be envisaged, the limit of the City itself, whose outline on the map must be remembered. An outline which, in a romantic lapse, one may observe to represent the sculptured figure of a man—chin forward, knee and shoulder braced as though setting out on some quest into the future —emerging from a vast plinth that has borne him, a mass of heterogeneous weight and shape that seems to represent all the complexities and experiences of the old and tried conglomerate City itself.

Now this City must be inspected in detail, the form and the feeling of its diverse streets set on the mind's backcloth. Start with Pimlico's home of the people, for this was to be the most heavily bombed area as it was the most filled with the houses of the people. Many of these streets fanning out behind Victoria station have a dingier, poorer aspect than the pillared and porticoed quietudes of Belgravia a little to the north. Much sooted London brick, much grey and falling plaster. In parts bleak, treeless, impregnated with the brownish, fogged grey that is London's real substance and against whose monotony the buses so magnificently drive their red. Yet, though much of the façade may be poor, there is in Pimlico a good humanity abroad. In the windows the monotony ceases, the curtains are of all sizes and shapes and colours, there is an infinity of different decorative devices to be perceived dimly through the windows: there is the impression that here not a few families but many people live. And in some parts, rising out of this relic of Victorian London, stand the great new estates of flats, as at Millbank or at Dolphin Square, where the scene becomes massive and planned but none the less human. These, however, are as yet exceptional, and the true Pimlico sprawls out Victorian and at first sight bleak; but here people live, it is a place of residence even if it is not grand; and if the soot clings too easily and if the railway does run too near the backyard—then there are compensations, for the pram's out in the alley and the washing's on the line, the steps scrubbed and the house in order, there's a square round the corner with trees in it and a pub with beer in it and a lively line of barrows lending an affection to the upper end of Lupus Street.

The weather, too—one must not forget the weather, for bombs fell in all weathers and the tired people woke and struggled through gusty February wetness and the brown slush of snows, through dusty days of full summer when in the evening the sun cast a red melancholy to the rise of the sirens, through days of pure cruel spring weather and nights of great moonlit beauty, through black soaking rain and in sweet intolerable sunshine. One is inclined to look back on an air-raid season too much as a wrapped-up parcel of events without relation to the real, nostalgic feeling of the day. When people meet they say: 'Good morning —a bit milder, isn't it?' Or: 'This *cold*!' Or whatever the weather signifies. These are not so much platitudes as the vital response of animal sensitivity to climate, they are perhaps the most important words spoken during the whole day, they express the first feeling of people; and even in a city, with all its artificialities and reasoning, the sniffing of the weather has a transcendental effect on the emotions of the day. So, bombs never fell in a vacuum of brick and stone and metal. They fell in streets of houses where that day the air smelt of this memory or that, where the season was prevalent.

How should one think of another part of Westminster, say the green part of the parks, of Hyde Park, the Green Park and St. James's Park? In the spring, fluorescently green in war as in peace? Or in the autumn, with late October as the season and the plane leaves thick and brown and golden on the paths, shussshing under our feet, blowing in crisp eddies, mounting for a time unswept, for the sweepers had gone to war? Or the barren winter parks, with the air wet and cold, the clay streaming on the gun emplacements and the rain beading the cord and yellow notice that mark off the site of an unexploded bomb?

The West End. From Piccadilly up Shaftesbury Avenue to the top reaches of Theatreland, down to Trafalgar Square with no fountains, in and around the streets that were once a glitter of amusement and in war were darkened, so that the only sign of a big restaurant bright inside with light would be the torch of its commissionaire hesitant and dim in the porch of a darkened door. No neon signs and bulbed electric messages shone down on Eros—the little famous figure soon became a shrouded obelisk of sandbag. Other statues were removed, some remained and assumed first a sackcloth of sandbags and later a more solid armour of concrete or brick. Through this centre of London's social traffic there pass some 450,000 people a day, to the great concrete and stone-built shops of Regent Street, to variegated Oxford Street, to Pall Mall's massive Clubland, to the theatres, the cinemas, the tea-shops, the restaurants, the hotels—in fact to such a cosmopolis and such a conglomerate of different kinds of building and type of interest that the scene cannot be defined, only implied in the broad landmarks of such places as Piccadilly with its Green Park railings disappeared, as Trafalgar Square with long low windowless shelters of red brick grown on its slate-dark pavements, as all the other familiar streets where strange hooded lights glinted at night, where khaki and air-force blue became more and more the passing colour, where blast-walls were built and sandbags were piled and where as the time of dishevelment advanced great gaps appeared, where wooden boarding took the flash from the windows and in the weathering of the storm the bright paint faded.

To the east of this lie the smaller Streets of Soho, the lanes round Covent Garden, the Strand of garish memory, the curious geography of the Adelphi with its waterside streets, its mammoth office buildings and underneath those huge, dismal arches; and still farther east there is the Temple and the first faint breath of the character of the City of London in that district by the Law Courts where St. Clement Danes and St. Mary-le-Strand grace with their white spires the highway to St. Paul's. A strange sector of the town, extending in a quarter of a mile from the spaghetti shops of Soho through winding warehouse lanes like Shelton Street to the labyrinthine slopes by the embankment.

At the bottom of the Strand the picture again changes with Whitehall and the offices of Government, a different city within the City and again peopled with a different population. Within each monumental façade lay then an atmosphere of war secrets, of the ubiquitous whispered *security'*, and here rolls of barbed wire and pill-boxes and reinforced sentry positions arose; here, too, arose one of the most severe problems of Civil Defence in Westminster, for each separate ministry and office had to guard its own 'security' and because of this maintained a separate A.R.P. staff, closing its gates to the regular services unless some incident should be severe enough to warrant a special (and of course delayed) invitation. The Houses of Parliament regarded themselves equally as a separate and secure entity, and within the miles of passageway and the many courts an intricate organization of civil defenders kept watch. For the A.R.P. authorities, this whole official colony became an island. And from a general view, Whitehall became by its nature the centre of war planning, a place where famous figures came and went, where radio masts on the Admiralty skyline took on new significance, and where ominously there arose the concrete embattlements of giant underground citadels for the carrying on of war in time of the City's danger. Of these underground fortresses there were two in the Whitehall area—a squarish sand-coloured pile like a Nigerian fort on the edge of the Horse Guards Parade, and the Fortress of the War Office lurking low and dark grey behind eighteenth-century Gwydyr House; these were linked—it was breathed—with deep subterranean passages. Yet above ground one could see little, Whitehall only took on a more martial air and the scarlet of the Life Guards changed to khaki. Yet the immensity of the Government Offices seemed to dwarf both the little martial goings-on down in the street and the bombs themselves.

Whitehall stood with massive indifference, preserving its memory of peacetime ceremonial.

At the edge of this security quarter stands the great Abbey against whose pious stone there could be seen an ordinary vista of antlike shelters and later the crawling black snakes of Fire Service pipeline. Behind lay Victoria Street and the Abbey district, more offices gradually changing to factories towards the embankment and the Vauxhall Bridge Road. Again a complicated and various district, with great mills like the Hovis Mill, great offices like those of the I.C.I. in Millbank, great housing estates, the Westminster Hospital and farther west in Pimlico the Railway Yards leading from Victoria Station. All these and other landmarks are woven into the general pattern of houses and offices and shops.

To the north-west of Victoria lies Belgravia, a prosperous name that graced the annals of the past century with an air of decorous aristocracy. Belgravia of the wider roads, of fine squares whose great houses and pillared porticoes reflect an elderly amplitude, now perhaps a little faded, but still evocative of the carriage, the Reception, the grand gaslight, the high noon of the street sweeper: Belgravia thus of solid houses that were to withstand moderately well, but not so well as concrete and steel, the visitations from above.

Thence up by Lowndes Street and Lowndes Square to Knightsbridge and farther west to embrace another residential district of prosperous building; and part of that spacious area of exhibitions laid out in the mid-nineteenth century, of which the Royal Albert Hall marks the crossing of the Westminster province into Kensington Gardens. Thereafter, from the Broad Walk eastward to Park Lane there is parkland and the Serpentine, a green expanse of many acres patrolled during the Blitz not by wardens but by the police; and an expanse whose trees and walks and undulations provided some exercise in the search for unexploded bombs.

Park Lane introduces to the City yet another atmosphere, Mayfair—and the Lane itself provides a skyline to show how this province of the more wealthy is furnished not only with great mansions of the past but also with immense new blocks of flats and hotels well reinforced with steel. This matter of steel reinforcement provided always a main consideration under bombardment, again and again it proved its worth. The great hotels and compilations of flats provided useful shelter. However, Mayfair produced one risk particular to its mansions—in that many of these were left empty, and so became vulnerable to the incendiary burning undetected in the quiet upper stories.

INTRODUCTION

Mayfair is not only a district of large properties. For large properties needed servants and coaching space—so there is the life of the mews and of such places as Shepherd's Market also to be examined. Again such centres of fashionable shopping as Bond Street, with its large expanses of plate glass to be splintered, and Regent Street, and Piccadilly.

South of Piccadilly, where the suave streets of Mayfair give way to the green of the Green Park, a further character asserts itself—the centremost personality of the City as it is geographically near the centre; the part of Royal Palaces and of the royal roadway of the Mall. Here set among the parks—the Green Park, the St. James's Park and the Palace Gardens—stands Buckingham Palace. And nearby there is the royal residence of Marlborough House and the Palace of St. James's. And here again the impression that the buildings are massive and impregnable must be tempered with a view not only of fairly solid stonework, but also of much brick fronted with plaster, and with much eighteenth-century building lying around St. James's. Apart from some steel-framed buildings, and some safer yet vulnerable stone and brick piles, there is thus contained here much of the well-proportioned Georgian residue whose black-washed London brick and venerable plaster will disintegrate nearly into dust at the stroke of even a fifty kilo bomb. London is a conglomerate city, only in limited areas does a planned character evolve. One can deduce an impression of this or that district—but it will seldom express the intricate truth. For instance, at the top of Whitehall there stands the Portland stone façade of the Admiralty; opposite the Edwardian baroque immensity of the War Office, built of brick and only faced with stone; then, within a few yards, Gwydyr House, a Georgian mansion of immaculate brick and austere cream decoration; and—a few yards on to the other side of the War Office—suddenly the sober skyline of Whitehall is broken by the brittle carving and false turreting of a small mass of tall, narrow, highly decorated late Victorian shops and offices, buildings more in the character of the raffish Strand; and opposite, the concrete and chromium of the Whitehall Theatre. There within a stone's throw lies a clue to the true character of London's intricacy, a more real cross-section of the background of events than any generalization of name—Whitehall, Pimlico, Covent Garden—could define.

In the recapitulation of the war's experience within such an intricate geography, one is faced with a further intricacy in terms of time. The war lasted nearly six years. At every moment during that period there was the possibility of attack from the air. At certain moments the attack came, and at certain other periods of lull the life of the City changed character according to other contemporary developments. How, then, would it be best to record both events and experiences? In the straight order of time as we know it, chronologically from the first civic preparations before the Munich Agreement until the time of the final casualties from fireworks at the celebration of the Eastern Victory? Or would it be better to start with the narrative of attack and then spend the long lull period of 1942 and 1943 in an assessment of behaviour and contemporary emotion in the light of Blitz experience, and in a review also of the civil defence organization as it was first conceived and as it thereafter set out to be?

The latter course has been chosen. The war was a period of constant change and development: from the point of view of this City, the years may be marshalled into five fairly clear phases. They would appear to be: first, what has been called the 'phoney' war and the 'sitzkrieg' and entails the period from Mr. Chamberlain's speech on the 3rd September 1939 until the 30th August 1940, when the first few incendiaries marked for Westminster the beginning of the period called the Blitz: next then the long period of heavy bombardment from early September 1940 until the 11th of May 1941; after that the time generally known as the 'Lull', which continued from May 1941 until January 1944 with only sporadic air-raid warnings and very slight damage; fourthly, what has been called the 'Little Blitz', dating from mid-January 1944 until mid-March of that year, a period of several sharp and short but quite destructive raids by piloted plane; fifthly, the attack by unpiloted missile, which began in the middle of June 1944 with the flying bomb and gradually developed into the attack by long-range rocket, the period of danger not ending until late March in 1945. Those are the five periods. Their dates refer exactly to periods when Westminster was actually struck by bombs; though the periods of general warning and alert may be spread days or weeks wider.

It is, then, the intention of this book first to record the active narrative of the Blitz 1940–41; then to speak of London life in the Lull and take this breathing space to assess the historical development of all the organizations for civil defence; and then to continue with the second act of the narrative, the resumption of bombing in 1944 and the incursion thereafter of the pilotless inventions. In short, a nine months' Blitz period, a two and a half year lull with the pre-Blitz year added, and thirdly the last year and few months of resumed attack.

In the autumn of 1945, with the war ended and already falling into a sure but steadily misting perspective, there could be seen on one of the yellow columns of the Lyceum Theatre portico a torn poster

INTRODUCTION

inviting recruits for what was in 1939 called the Auxiliary Fire Service. The red fire had faded to a phantom pink, the blue-black uniforms of the firemen was weathered in six years to the grey of ghosts. This poster must have been set up in the first days of the war, in the long-lost summer days of September 1939, when disaster on a Wellsian scale was expected. And then, a few yards from this poster on the newly leafless branches of a row of young trees, there hung what appeared to be white and frozen streams of sleet. These were the remains of streamers thrown down in celebration of Victory in the summer of 1945. They, too, the gaily coloured streamers, had been washed in so short a time of their colour and now hung as white as winter on the black branches. How long it took the poster to fade, how short a time the streamers!

With this in mind, and in delectation of the mighty atom, the story shall begin with the arrival on these streets of the smallest of all bombs, and one that behaved according to its size—the fall of a one kilo thermite incendiary.

PART ONE

THE BLITZ

THE BLITZ

The first bombs fell just before eleven o'clock on the night of the
30th of August, 1940. They fell in Belgravia—four one kilo
incendiaries, four of the smallest units of fire devised for the
Luftwaffe, each a foot-length candle of smooth silver magnesium fused
and fired by a dark pith of thermite. Little bombs, efficient in their
showers, but in this case greater in impact than their size merited; for
the impact was made not only upon the streets of Belgravia but also
upon the minds of the citizens on watch. The long, long series of lessons
that were to be learnt throughout the next six years had begun. The
days of theory were over. The practical bomb had arrived.

The night was clear, it was high summer and the approaching climax
of a season that had begun with the fall of France and was to end with
the invasion of England. Approach is the keyword of those times. The
ears of London listened towards the south and the east, they listened for
the sounds of Goering's sweep of the southern airfields, for the chattering
of those dog-fights that the newspapers every day brought farther inland. For a while they listened in vain. Then—the first guns. A distant
resonance on the warm summer air. It seemed, at the time, very distant,
still incredible, still separate. Such sounds had nothing to do with
London. Yet they approached—the unbelievable was perhaps to
occur. Night reconnaissance planes purred at a great and solitary height
at the top of the vast night sky doming London. Yet the old division
in the mind remained, the division between reason and real expectation: reason said that the approach would accelerate to embrace
London, that bombs would fail to disorganize the defences, that para-
chuted automata of the Wehrmacht would descend to invest the capital
from within, that submarine lanes across the Channel would direct to
these shores the shipped bulk of that huge and yet invincible grey
machine; but still in the forefront of the London mind, and of the minds
of those citizens of Westminster who form the subject of this record, still
the human and the vague thought persisted: 'It won't happen, not here,
and not to us.' So they continued to walk the streets at night. So when
the sirens echoed few took shelter. So in Westminster on that Friday

night of the 30th, despite mouth-to-mouth reports that six days before
there had occurred in other boroughs the first light scattering of bombs
on London proper—so they were still living their ordinary night-life
of the black-out, many at home, a few walking home. The streets were
tense, there was an undercurrent of the alert: but pervading this the
casual necessity of doing the normal thing.

In such surroundings, then, the first four bombs fell. Take one. It fell
near Belgrave Square. A warden patrolling round the corner heard it—
an empty clattering as it bounced on and off a roof, the final thud as it
came to rest down somewhere in the street. The warden ran towards
the sound, and as he ran saw for the first time the reflection of the
incendiary white light, saw it set off the dark corner of the street, saw
it bring into cold and clinical relief the façades that caught its reflection.
He rounded the corner and saw a bright glare sizzling from a basement
area. The area gate was locked. He had to climb across the pointed
railings. Somebody handed him a stirrup pump. It was coiled, its strap
buckled fast. The bomb burned fiercer. The warden agitated the strap
free—but still nobody had brought water. For some seconds the warden,
as prompt as he himself could have been, stood waiting with the useless
snake dry in his hand. Then a bucket of water came. Somebody pumped.
The bomb was showered, began to subside. And all through these
moments—a tense time for it was the first time—all through and over
and over again a man kept saying: 'You'll let me have my bucket back,
won't you? You'll let me have my bucket back . . . ?' A short while later
a pump of the London Fire Service arrived to certify the end of that,
the first lesson.

Lessons they were, inevitably. To keep the stirrup pump unlashed,
to have water ready drawn, to begin the long business of seeing that
locks were kept unlocked and the knowledge now that these bombs
might not be as fearsome as had been predicted, for it must be remembered that such incendiaries were until then in the warden's mind
generators of colossal heat, blinding, unapproachable affairs that called
for asbestos shields and dark goggles over the eyes. Though in relation
to the future this was a small incident, yet it was intrinsically the first
thread in the pattern of experience. And the incident ended its minor
importance with a true provincial panache—the warden who had put it
out came from Post 14 and yet, horror of all horrors, the bomb had
fallen within the province of Post 12. How then should it be reported?
Whose bomb was it? . . . the dispute began there and then, and it
continued for days, the first of what was to become a classic wrangle,
the proud and tetchy fight for the possession of scars.

Three hours later a few more light incendiaries fell, striking, among other places, in the vicinity of the Royal Mews and on the roof of Taylor's Depository; ominous little bombs, for within the month Buckingham Palace was to be the special target of selective bombing of a more severe kind, and Taylor's large Depository the scene of much fortuitous fire and destruction. Again these few bombs brought with them their lesson. The incendiary on the Depository, for instance, extinguished itself on a tarred space of roof, showing the wardens for the first time that such incendiaries tended to smother themselves rather than ignite tarred surfaces, such as roads and roof expanses; and secondly, this particular bomb, which was first seen from some distance away, demonstrated the need to take a bearing between some landmark and the place of first observation and thus mark more exactly the position of a bomb whose colour and light might itself be shielded.

The next night—nothing happened. The sirens sounded as usual— they had sounded pretty regularly since the first days of August—but in Westminster the wardens, pitched now to a point of the alert that almost *wished* for a bomb, relieved too perhaps in the knowledge that they were able to deal with what had been so far a perilously unknown quantity, these anxious watchers watched in vain. Nothing to report. And the same the night after. And thus for several nights.

Until at ten o'clock on the fourth, Lowndes Square suddenly broke alive with a louder thud than before, and some seconds later a patrolling warden came running into his post with the news of 'a large crater'. This was new. The wires began to hum. The message travelled to the Westminster Report Centre at City Hall and from thence out to the Depots. Soon into Lowndes Square drove a formidable array of rescue vehicles—in all three lorry loads of Heavy Rescue teams, two cars of stretcher parties, one ambulance, and one First Aid motor-car. They drew up on the roadway near No. 21. They found there a small hole made by an unexploded anti-aircraft shell—and nothing more. Nobody dead, nobody injured, no worthwhile damage. One by one the vehicles left. And, apart from a hole in the roof and a hole in the road, all that remained of the incident was a remark in the official record: 'Inexperienced reporting'. This was an accurate description—it was inexperienced. But no blame should be attached, for experience had only then begun. Again a lesson was learnt. And some minutes later another shell came to earth, this time up in the West End, and this time it exploded . . . providing thus for the services a further entry into the annals of experience.

For another two nights wardens patrolled incidentless. Above, there was gunfire and the sound of the high German invader. These sounds, and the few incidents that had scattered the streets during the week, might be likened to the scattered scraping of bow-strings as the orchestra tuned up; for the night of the seventh of September was on its way, the night when the first great chord of the London Overture smashed its steel music on to the auditorium of streets and houses and people.

Here for a moment, in what might seem now the breathless pause before the event, it would be well to dissert upon one truth of high importance in assessing and appreciating the feeling of that time, and indeed of all other times throughout the war. It must be always remembered, simply but constantly, that at the time nobody knew what was going to happen next. Now we know. In retrospect the period seems neatly parcelled into events and into lulls without event. But then, obviously, it was different. Perhaps London was going to suffer the fate of Rotterdam, perhaps like all capitals so far except Warsaw she was to remain inviolate but slightly peppered. Perhaps there was to be an invasion, perhaps there was not. Perhaps that first incendiary was going to blow up or blind that first attacking warden, perhaps it was not. Perhaps that 'large crater' concealed some inestimable danger beneath, perhaps it did not. And on the sunny morning of the seventh of September—perhaps that sun was to set to the tune of a few shell-bursts and perhaps it was not. This is of course very obvious. But it is easy, in reading history, to forget the fact of ignorance before the event. It must always be first in the mind.

So then, the dawning of that fatal seventh. One of the fairest days of the century, a day of clear warm air and high blue skies. Over the capital on the eve of its threatened siege there dawdled a forgotten sense of peace. The hours on such a day in high summer seem to extend themselves in their invitation to leisure, the trees in full leaf cast in their dusty shadows a truth of peace greater than transient human wars; and in many men's minds that day—whether they were listening for gunfire at the doorway of their posts, or tiredly working through the office day after a night with the Home Guard, or with the Saturday afternoon free were walking in the park, or just sitting at home with the windows open and the week drawing to a long close, an uneasy close with the siren's acceleration and the tensening of newspaper headlines that breathed of the Approach—in many men's troubled, taut minds there was yet an appreciation of that queer lullaby of peace brought with the weather, an evocation of London summers of the past, when striped awnings shaded the shopping and geraniums bloomed red in window boxes freshly painted and blistered in the sun, when bands played in the royal parks and canaries slept in the tenement windows, when this central part of London was a fine and spacious vista of pale grey, black, green and scarlet.

Towards six o'clock the fiction of unease became fact, the man on the street learnt that something had been happening in the East End, something more significant than the ordinary tidings brought by the siren—and Report Centres and other official quarters knew that at last the Luftwaffe had struck hard, there and then, that afternoon, at London proper. The docks were ablaze. And as the sun set, those in the West End streets grew conscious of the unbelievable, for the sunset occurred not only in the accustomed west near Putney and Willesden, but also incredibly in the East over St. Paul's and where the City of London was held to lie. That was curious enough—but when the western skies had grown already dark the fierce red glow in the East stuck harshly fast and there was seen for the first time that black London roof-scape silhouetted against what was to become a monotonously copper-orange sky. So in Westminster they knew and they could see that something was on. Yet still it seemed curiously separate. This was yet happening in the East. There was still prevalent the concept of special targets for raiding bombers. A line of imagined strategy was drawn between the East and the West. The sky was lit up, fearsomely—but there was not the expected massed gunfire. So that, for Westminster, although the night began more tensely indeed than others, it was yet without action, without the feeling in fact of being attacked. Things were unusual, but there was yet no climax.

Then, just after eleven o'clock, the first high explosives fell—a stick of five bombs in the vicinity of Victoria Station and Victoria Street. People were killed. People were wounded. The powdered smell of smashed plaster and brick poisoned the air for the first time. Glass, illimitable, spread itself across the pavements and out over the road—it seemed to lie two or three inches thick. The peace was shattered, and the machine of defence went into action for its first real blooding.

It was an unlucky time—the public houses had just closed. Many people were out just then on the pavements, for at the end of the Vauxhall Bridge Road there was a busying of late night trams and buses. The iron replica of Big Ben stood then above a scene of stunned disaster and wounding, cries were heard from the neighbouring street, and in the great darkened railway station itself there occurred particular trouble. To this, then, came the ambulances and rescue parties for their first incident. The ambulances and stretcher parties were needed most; it was an open street affair; complicated rescue work was not called for. But all who drove there saw their first casualties. This first sight of blood and wounding is an experience sharp in its emotional effect, often physically affecting. People react, of course, according to their nature. Coldly in some, warmly in others. One girl ambulance driver, for instance, was sometimes physically sick back at the Depot after her night's work was done; she was able to hold on during the moments of needed action, but on relaxing afterwards was overcome with a delayed physical nausea. Others, at the other end of the scale, felt nothing, neither horror nor pity—yet underwent through this very coolness a mental disaffection, a self-condemnation for the lack of what they wished could be a capacity for pity.

That night several raiders drove high over Westminster and across farther west. They dropped in all about a dozen high explosive bombs in the City's area. In retrospect, and relatively to the greater raids to come, this was small stuff, a peppering. They were small bombs, too, weighing only fifty kilos. But each night, and each of those early nights in particular, must be regarded as a microcosm, a period of anxiety contained within itself and related only to the experience of the moment. It happened that of those dozen bombs, four hit Victoria Station. This, with news of the fairly accurate firing of the East End docks, suggested at the time that special targets could be accurately selected. It was unfortunate, too, that of the other damage important gas mains in Smith Square suffered and even more disastrously a key 6,000 volt high tension electrical cable. This twin exposure of the vulnerability of under-street utility lines brought thus its early lesson to the repair services involved. The Gas Company learnt the meaning of broken pipes and thick London clay sogging any immediate chances of clean repair; and for the electricians in this case it was a more severe lesson, because of all places in the City this was among the worst where a bomb could have dropped—it disturbed the main run of cables from a Bulk Supply Station bearing electricity bound for Whitehall. This bomb was of a delayed action type. It penetrated beneath the cables and lay there quiet. The supply company's emergency staff inspected the trouble— and then not long after the bomb exploded, damaging no fewer than twenty-six cables and destroying joints along the line. Cables were stretched and twisted and broken and tied into nightmare knots—but several remained alive—including the 6,000 volt high tension line. That taught another lesson—it gave evidence of the general toughness and resistance to damage of such cables even in these circumstances of phenomenal breakage.

So the next day, a Sunday, saw the various repair services go into action for the first time. The first surveys of damage were made, the first clearing of the streets and the first small traffic diversions. Meanwhile the skies to the south traced with white trails of fleece their dog-fights. German squadrons drove towards London—but Fighter Command fought a successful battle of interception. No bombs fell. Until nightfall. Then, between seven and eight o'clock a force of some two hundred bombers flew in to stir up the many great conflagrations still burning along the eastern docksides. And as before, some of these Heinkels and Dorniers came across and dropped a scattering of incendiaries and explosives in the Westminster City area. In the early part of the night only incendiaries were dropped; they caused a few fires, but none serious. Then, in accordance with the contemporary German tactic of spreading their fires with explosives, the heavier bombs began to fall. This time the aim was more dispersed—bombs fell from the Covent Garden area to Hyde Park, Pimlico and Exhibition Road, covering thus a vague line inland from the Thames. Among the more known buildings hit were the stables of the Cavalry at Knightsbridge Barracks, and the Royal Courts of Justice; a delayed action bomb fell in the grounds of Buckingham Palace. The Southern Railway suffered again with a direct hit on the bridge in Grosvenor Road. However, the most important incidents of the night were experienced in more populated areas—in Neal Street for instance, where a high explosive bomb hit one of the wholesale fruit premises in this vicinity of Covent Garden. It was a grave incident, and here the Heavy Rescue parties first showed their mettle. They were faced with a building of several stories collapsed completely and blocking the narrow street into which it had fallen. People were known to have been on the upper floors. To make matters worse, a large fire developed next door and rescue work was impeded, drenched, sodden by water from the fire-hoses. Overhanging debris was dangerously insecure and of great weight. In soaking rubble and with the firelight flaring over a street confused with the litter of vegetables and water and hoses and bricks and timber—in such conditions the rescue workers picked among the brise blocks of the devastated building and extricated the dead and the wounded.

Two important bombs fell in Shelton Street on the Holborn boundary and in Sussex Street. Both were of the delayed action type, and they gave the police and wardens their first experience of evacuation on a large scale. The Sussex Street bomb sent as many as two hundred people from their homes to the neighbouring Rest Centres, two school buildings held in readiness for the homeless. And here again the dominant note of the time is heard—problems revealing themselves and experience feeling itself. For instance, the problem of these delayed action bombs had never been fully envisaged. Up to that time, in the official prescience of air-raids, the gas bomb had taken first place, the incendiary second, the high explosive a bad third and the delayed action bomb lay very much in the hinterland of speculation. There were intelligent reasons for this, and reasons of Intelligence. In the first place, gas was a subject that invited the most complete technological exploration—most was known about the limits of scientific discovery in the field of toxic war gases. And again, if gas had been dropped or sprayed, it would have presented in a populated area the greatest civic problems (though not necessarily the greatest number of casualties). Gas was an obsession of the early days. Warsaw had escaped it, Rotterdam, too—but that was no proof that the weapon was not being reserved for a heavier punch at London. In the case of incendiaries, a common-sense appreciation held that fire was both an economical and intensely destructive weapon; there were remembered the historical associations of fire with the investing of cities, the sackings and burnings of all time, and it was reasonable to suppose that this traditional corruption might be continued. But in the case of high explosives, the simple fact had to be faced that least was known about these, least could be known. It was easier to invent and produce quite unknown types of explosive bombs in relative secrecy. The Spanish Civil War, with all its primary lessons, had been over for some years. Polish, Dutch, Belgian and French cities had suffered explosive attack—but the opportunities for detailed survey were not many. And last on this list comes the question of the delayed action bomb, whose supposed potentialities might be illustrated by the fact that the area for evacuation was put at a radial distance of no less than 600 yards from the site of the bomb! It can be imagined what a situation might have been caused by the dropping of only a dozen of these at scattered points. . . . Added to this, there was no proper organization envisaged for reconnaissance of such bombs; and there were only a handful of Royal Engineers attached to the Westminster area who were equipped to immobilize the fuses. However, as from the 13th September this nominal complement was considerably increased—officers and men from other parts of the country were called in and a complete bomb disposal company was formed, whose province included all the area north of the Thames: later, a Divisional officer holding the rank of Captain was appointed to each Civil Defence Group.

The Sussex Street incident gave a disturbing picture of what might happen. Two hundred people in this instance were now without homes.

They were easily absorbed into the L.C.C. Rest Centres; but one could well see that much more accommodation would have to be found if the situation developed on lines that could now be anticipated. Meanwhile, at the point where the bomb fell, the eyes of those rescue squads present saw a scene that was later to prove an every-night nonentity. But then it was new. Men's eyes were opened, they walked warily over the broken brick of their education. Here at Sussex Street, for instance, was a smallish crater, with the bomb disappeared beneath. A gas main had been ignited, a water main torn. Vaults used as shelters were slowly flooding. One rescue man went down with a candle and saw the fantastic—several people huddled together, afraid to come out, yet certain also that with the rising water they would be drowned. A few feet away from them a sharklike fin protruded from the water, a dull metal shape gloomy in the candlelight, the fin of the bomb itself standing on its nose and half submerged. The shelterers were brought out quickly and evacuated. Council officers had arrived in the 'Old Grey Mare' (a grey-painted car used by those men hastily allocated to bomb reconnaissance) and the main evacuation ordered. The bomb blew empty houses into the sky at six o'clock that morning.

They were empty houses—but for one man, a late night arrival who had climbed unseen up to his room and had gone to bed in sweet ignorance. He was lucky enough to have only half of his particular house blown away, and luckier still to have chosen to sleep in the half that remained. There he lay in half a bedroom. He was brought down by ladder. He provided yet another tactical lesson, the lesson of the strange and individual and quite unpredictable happening that was to permeate the character of bombing throughout the war. He was, in fact, the City's first freak.

Thus two nights: in the minds of West-Enders, of Whitehall and of the people of Pimlico, there remained no more than a blurring of the line that had separated them from the burning east. Now the people felt attacked. After two nights there was little doubt that there would be a third; for although at this point a general siege of weeks was not envisaged—for then one was more inclined to think of short and sharp engagements, a protracted investing from the air had not then been heard of—nevertheless the shelters came to be used, the blacked-out streets were left empty and strangely dead. And from the severely struck East End there began a nightly inflow of shelterers attracted by the heavier buildings and the deep tube stations of the west.

So was introduced a further problem, perhaps the greatest problem of all for the civic authorities, the problem of providing for a shelter life as opposed to the facility for temporary refuge. Shelters had, of course, been built, and good ones—but up to that time the Ministry of Home Security had been led to believe that raids would be devastating in scale but short in time, so that consequently all sheltering accommodation had been organized on this hypothesis. Even after the loss of Dunkirk, and when it was fully realized that the Luftwaffe was equipping the northern shore of France with new and extensive airfields, airfields little more than half an hour's journey from the British capital—even then it was still ruled that raids would be short. No provision, therefore, was made for the long hours that people were to spend breathing and eating and sleeping together in shelters. It began to appear possible that the whole inner fabric of what were otherwise excellent constructions might have to be revised and conceived in terms of living. However, for the time being, no move was made, there was no certain evidence that the Germans intended to maintain this weight of nightly bombing—though now indeed it began to appear possible.

This thought was forming in the minds of the people as from then on nightly they took to the shelters. More and more decided to leave their beds and go underground, to the public shelters requisitioned in the basements of large buildings, to the crypts of churches, to the vaults underneath the pavements in front of their own houses, to the trenches constructed in the squares and parks, to the brick surface shelters—and as the days went on to the deep platforms of the underground tube railway. They began to carry their blankets with them, they slept on the floors if they could get to sleep. Then there were no bunks, often no lights, no cups of tea, only chemical lavatories—the picture is one of candlelight, of floors a gritty buff with the sand that had leaked from sandbags, and of men and women and children sitting and squatting and lying huddled against the protective walls, throwing forlorn and depressive shadows above them; a time of raised eyes and apprehension, of ears opened to the lance-like descending whistle of high explosives (a sound that made the sky seem so very high and wide) and the dull, smothered boom that had shattered some house somewhere away out in the darkened streets.

On the Monday night of the ninth the bombing weight was again slightly increased. Charing Cross railway bridge was hit, and the train service interrupted; on the following night Victoria Station was again struck, this time in the central section of the carriage sidings: so that after four nights the railways were becoming aware of the difficulties that lay in store for them and conscious of the target that they then seemed to offer. Perhaps they did form a target; though this is difficult to state. During those nights bombs were scattered over a large area of the City, with perhaps a tendency towards the region of Victoria and Pimlico. The question of whether a night bomber aimed at a special target, or dropped his load without discrimination came for the first time to everybody's lips; nobody knew; certainly there was little gunfire to worry the bombardier. Yet bombs fell on houses, streets, and in the parks, disrupting services and destroying homes and killing people —though there were no incidents of what might be called major disaster.

The adjudication of what is major disaster and what is a minor incident becomes difficult in human terms to decide. No disaster can be greater than the death or the maiming of a single person. No destruction can be mourned more than the destruction of one home and its well-loved rooms. But each of these losses is limited to an intimate circle; and there were many more losses of a private nature than any other. In these pages, though sympathetically it is felt that no disaster can be greater than such individual suffering, there is obviously not room to record them; so that 'major disasters' must be taken to mean destruction that harms at one blow many members of the community or the community as a whole—that is, multiple loss of life, or the loss of buildings and institutions of significance to all the people.

Thus no major disasters occurred, but the detail of the life was forming. Different sorts of incidents occurred. The magazine in Hyde Park was set alight by incendiaries. The vast pile of Somerset House was hit, giving an internal wardens' staff their first experience. And in Regent Street there fell a very heavy delayed action bomb.

This last incident occurred within a few yards of Piccadilly Circus. It was after three o'clock in the morning, so that the streets were clear of the crowds that norm ally made the Circus area a place of high responsibility. However, the Piccadilly Hotel was affected and had to be evacuated. It is interesting, as a by-product of this bomb, to note that during the evacuation a Guards officer, leaning on a stick and dressed in no more than pyjamas and dressing-gown, happened to tell a warden that all that remained to him in the world since his return from the battle of Narvik was contained in a suitcase which lay above in his bedroom on the fifth floor. The warden immediately went up to the bedroom, retrieved the suitcase and gave it to the officer. These times were soon after the Dunkirk evacuation; there was a natural sympathy with the Army; but the episode was symptomatic of a more general attitude —for throughout the months to come wardens or rescue men often risked their lives to bring out possessions prized by the people they had rescued. At such moments, having saved a life, and seeing the plight of the rescued, it seemed that at all costs life should be made worth living as well as merely preserved.

Meanwhile, the Regent Street bomb was cordoned off. It lay high and dry on the roadway, in full view of anyone who could get near enough to see. It differed from other unexploded bombs in that the majority tended to bury themselves. This one lay exposed and cordoned until the next day, when Royal Engineers arrived to proceed with its disposal. They used a device for steaming out the explosive mixture from the shell of the bomb. Rubber tubing stretched from the bomb along the street in two directions. At one end the steaming compressor was fixed, at the other a receiving apparatus. Slowly then, as the hours went by, as the bomb lay dormant but ready to explode at some moment recorded only by its inside mechanism, slowly the poisonous filling was emptied through the long rubber tubes. But the process was too slow. At a quarter past six on the following evening the bomb exploded. Muffled then by sandbag walls, blast caused small damage—the destruction for many hundreds of yards round of the fine plate glass windows of Regent Street's shops, and a few chips in the stone façades of the Quadrant buildings, such as the Café Royal.

On the next day, a Wednesday, Whitehall was hit for the first time. Towards five o'clock in the afternoon an anti-aircraft shell dropped and exploded on the south side of the Horse Guards Avenue, fifty yards from Whitehall. The internal air-raid staff of the War Office went into operation. There were some street casualties, though not many: workmen constructing an underground tunnel to the Fortress were injured, a policeman found a piece of shrapnel as long as a fountain pen embedded in his arm—after he had been working on the injured for five minutes. But luckily the streets had been emptied by the sirens—in those first few days cover was taken automatically, for the scene was unfamiliar, the expectations unlimited. But this proved to be the single incident, in itself as isolated as perhaps a bad motor smash, and soon the afternoon was resumed.

Nothing more happened till the nightfall barrage when the enemy bombers came droning over again and when a momentous event shook London. A momentous sound that sent a chattering, smashing, blinding thrill through the London heart—for that was the night the barrage went up. As the planes came over, guns started up from every side. The night was filled suddenly with the crack of gunfire, the whine of shells, the keen yellow flashes lighting at the mouths of the guns. Gunfire there had been, but nothing like this. A violent medley of angry sounds, urgently accumulating like the barking of a pack of dogs, a rattling of pompoms and a booming of great naval guns. It was London's first curtain of gunfire. Up till then there had been sporadic shooting, but those on the streets felt largely undefended. Now the night was filled with energy and the good sense of hitting back. Morale kicked up high. The whispers went round: 'Destroyers in the Thames . . . heavy naval guns mobile on the railway . . . bringing up batteries of 'em on lorries. . . .' Those on duty in the streets and those resting and listening in their homes and in the shelters took new heart. The game was going into full swing.

To such a tune bombs continued to be dropped, though—one felt—less easily. In Westminster a few high explosives fell, hitting among other places the premises of the Corps of Commissionaires in Maiden Lane. This happened to be a delayed action bomb, it penetrated in a straight perpendicular down through the stories to end up in the basement; a good round hole was cut in the bedroom of several floors where men were sleeping; it is said that not even the bedclothes were disturbed and the commissionaires continued to sleep. But at half-past seven the next evening passers-by in the Strand were startled by a loud report and a shower of golden coins raining down from the empty skies; the report was the exploding of the time-bomb, the coins no more than buttons from the button store of the Corps of Commissionaires.

On the following night the sirens wailed at dusk—a mournful music that as the days wore on was to charge the twilight air with a ritual apprehension—but the weight of bombs that fell on Westminster was rather less than before, although the number of bombers passing overhead and the crackling, whining thunder of the new barrage filled the night with a sense of activity in no way decreased. A harmless incendiary fell on the Houses of Parliament—their first bomb—and some windows in Westminster Abbey were blown in by an anti-aircraft shell. Within the tense labyrinth of Westminster's streets private tragedies continued to occur—none perhaps more tragic than the wounding of a man who was out on the pavement of Northumberland Avenue. He had the calf blown off one of his legs. And his legs were perhaps the one worldly possession this man prized. He was a tramp.

The next morning dawned cloudy—cloudy, heavy, and eventful. At eleven o'clock a German bomber flew in down below the clouds, below the balloon barrage, and spurting in between two balloons set his course straight along the Mall and dived for Buckingham Palace. His intentions were undoubted, his aim was good—but the results finally less fortunate for the Luftwaffe than for England. Two explosives fell on the red gravel of the internal quadrangle of the Palace, one through the roof of the Royal Chapel and one delayed action bomb in the roadway in front of the forecourt. To assess the position of the quadrangle bombs, one needs to remember that the Palace is roughly square, its Mall façade forming the one well-known side of this square and the quadrangle behind it occupying a large proportion of the Palace area. So that there was plenty of room in the quadrangle for two small high explosives. They dropped in the south-western corner, blasting the tall glass windows of the ground floor Ambassadors' Corridor and splintering the tall portraits hanging there. They blasted also the windows of the western side of the quadrangle in which is situated the immense and pillared Grand Entrance. Inside, debris covered the crimson carpet, and a light dust clouded the white walls with their gilded decorations. A water main was broken, flooding part of the basement. But no heavy damage was suffered. Within a hundred yards, in a room on the first floor, their Majesties were sitting. They had arrived some minutes before the bomb fell. They were taking tea.

Less fortunate was the Royal Chapel. The bomb, again a small one, penetrated the roof and the floor, exploding in the basement. Four men at work here were injured, one of whom later died. The chapel itself was wrecked, though the actual structure held firm. The only visible track of the bomb was the small hole of its entry through the square-decorated roof—but thereafter among the mahogany seats, the red and grey tapestried dado, all was churned up and blasted. A heavy alabaster pulpit was broken, the organ damaged, a fine tapestry thrown down from behind the altar: only the iron columns, tipped with their gold corinthian capitals, stood firm above the wreckage of sacred ornament and life.

Outside in the roadway the delayed action bomb had been causing trouble. Wardens had, of course, telephoned to the Report Centre for assistance, and soon the Rescue officers had arrived. The immediate necessity was to build a sandbag wall round the bomb to protect the Palace façade. One of the Rescue Service volunteered to do this, and soon a chain was formed delivering sandbags to him. So, laboriously, the officer and two rescue parties built a wall against time, a wall five feet thick and six feet high. The raid was still going on, bombs were falling and the smoke of fires could be seen. Sandbags were brought from a dump by the Royal Stables, manhandled across the forecourt. But in the urgent first minutes a small incident occurred that is well illustrative of the muddled, tense, yet extraordinarily phlegmatic spirit of the times. There, in front of the railing, lies the crater and the bomb. Wardens, sentries, police have quickly gathered. A Palace servant in a striped waistcoat can be seen in the distance, hurrying it happens for a sponge to cool the brow of a gentleman shocked by the recent explosions. By the bomb, the cry is raised for sandbags. A warden goes to the Royal Stables where there is known to be a dump. He is about to commandeer it when officials in charge question whether these particular sandbags should be used and suggest that the Rescue parties bring their own. A short argument evolves. Finally the warden prevails. These and no other sandbags shall be used—but not until the warden has there and then personally signed a chit acknowledging the receipt of, to be exact, five hundred and thirty-four sandbags! But that in passing. The real business of building the wall was in time completed. Later this Rescue officer received the George Medal for his work. He had conducted operations that had saved the Palace from greater damage. The bomb exploded eventually at twenty minutes to nine on the following morning, demolishing only a section of the black and gold Palace railings.

Otherwise, the morning was lively. Incendiaries were scattered over from Charing Cross to the Palace. The new Public Offices in Whitehall suffered a small fire; a dog ambled over to a crater in Eaton Square and sniffed at the unexploded bomb newly resident there. A busy little morning, gloomy, tense, Fridayish—in the sense of those Fridays that erupt instead of settling down, as is their quiescent function, for an ending to a week.

However, it was hardly a week that merited a week-end, and by that time few people were expecting any respite. The acceleration was on, the East End of London was known generally to have been very severely damaged, and although in the west the weight of bombs had been relatively slight, there was by now an accumulation of isolated damage that began to present a picture, as one drove in and out the streets, of a bombarded city. On the turning of a corner the smooth street scene would be suddenly disturbed, a collapsed house with its outcreeping morain of packed timber and lathes and brick and plaster would sprawl desolate and dead in the row of otherwise placid and unwinking houses. The glass would be swept up, or perhaps they would be still sweeping, and the other debris would be banked up clear of the road. Rescue parties would still be at work, digging after hours for the trapped, the near-living or the dead. Passing closer, the neighbouring houses would be seen to be not quite as placid as had first been imagined—their windows would stare blackly, their curtains might hang torn, tiles would be displaced, a householder would be seen carrying out sackfuls of plaster from a fallen ceiling. In other streets, where bombs had fallen on the roadway, a marked cordon would block the street-end and traffic would search for another way round; here, along the perspective, groups of men from the utility companies and from the City's Works Department would be beginning the long labour of clearing and mending that intricate breakage of power and telephone cables, of gas mains, of hydraulic power and water mains, of the deeper sewer conduits. And another part of this gradually densening pattern would be those houses that overnight had been transformed into strange black skeletons—throughout sometimes the length of their stories, often only on the upper floors: here the little incendiaries had got to work, leaving a blackened or collapsed façade festering still with a light steam as the Fire Service hoses delivered their last cooling water. These hoses, hundreds of yards of their winding water-dark snakes, were becoming a regular feature of the red night and the grey morning.

The morning streets had an unreal air; the City continued about its business, there was an atmosphere of normality in the traffic and the people going to work; but the undertone whispered, the memory of the firebells and the ambulances of the night, the sharp smells of burning and the poison of plaster-dust, the knowledge of the stretcher and the shroud. Though few people had by then seen the mutilated wounded and the quiet dead, there rested an unspoken presence on the air; it was unbelievable, impossible in these streets hurrying back to normal that live people had only a few hours before been torn and killed; yet the imagination belied the incredible, it was known that people did not necessarily die prettily, that wounding was not a neat and a clean affair, and that there was being entered into A.R.P. log-books a cruel, recurrent, most contemporary phrase: 'Pieces of flesh'.

That night—the night of the 13th—there occurred an incident spectacular in both the nature of its damage and in the fortuitous escape of great numbers of people from injury. One of the highest and largest blocks of flats in London received several direct hits. This was Queen Anne's Mansions, eleven stories of black Victorian brick occupied by many hundreds of tenants. This, then, was no steel and concrete block—it was more vulnerable, and in this case suffered damage of a most unusual nature. One of the bombs penetrated the roof and sliced down in a dead perpendicular for 140 feet through all of the eleven stories, leaving a precise knife-like cut in the very tall building. The bomb, in fact, destroyed two vertical sections, leaving on either side the walls of other sections intact. In view of the building's great height, the effect was extraordinary, there had suddenly appeared a narrow, neat well, sliced straight down the entire façade. It was not then of course as neat as it appeared later, the debris of eleven stories lay piled to a height of the second floor and sloped out across to the other side of the narrow Petty France, blocking an underground shelter beneath the opposite pavement and looking then, with its predominant debris of timber, like the residue of some wooden shack-house after the cyclone. In all, about twenty flats were completely demolished, but the residents escaped serious injury. They were sheltering in the inner corridors previously selected as shelters. It can well be imagined what a multiple disaster might have occurred had the bomb fallen elsewhere, or had it not cut down through the building so cleanly. As it was, the residents had to be evacuated, for an unexploded bomb lay on one of the floors. Some of the infirm and aged were taken away in cars and ambulances, and if they had glanced back at their huge home they might have seen the façade pitted with forbidden lights, for black-out curtains had been torn, and high up a glowing electric stove hung from the wreckage, a dangerous source of fire and perilously deciduous among that debris.

On the following afternoon three oil bombs dropped in Pimlico—one of them exploding unignited oil over the northern block of Thames House.

The next day and night were not eventful of serious incident—a few oil bombs were dropped in the afternoon, but the night was free of explosive damage. However, this minor respite was short-lived, for at noon on Sunday morning there developed another daylight attack in the neighbourhood of Buckingham Palace, and Londoners saw a memorable aerial battle between a Dornier and a Hurricane fighter that ended in the descent of both planes upon Westminster's streets. Here is the text of the combat report as written afterwards by the British pilot involved, a note of what happened at 20,000 feet, among a matter of some twenty Dorniers, one or all of which were attacking Buckingham Palace.

'In the attack made by No. 504 Squadron I attacked the right flank machine from quarter to astern. Pieces flew from the wings and a flame appeared in the port wing but went out again. After breaking away I climbed up to a single D.O.215 and made two quarter attacks. Pieces flew off. My windscreen was now splashed with black oil. I attacked a third time and a member of the crew baled out. On my fourth attack from the port beam a jar shook my starboard wing as I passed over the E/A and I went into an uncontrollable spin. I think the E/A must have exploded beneath me. I baled out and as I landed I saw the Dornier hit the ground by Victoria Station ½ mile away.'

Parts of the German plane fell in Vauxhall Bridge Road and on a jeweller's shop in Victoria Station Yard, this latter causing a fire. The engine of the Hurricane penetrated six feet into the roadway opposite Fountain Court at the southern junction of Buckingham Palace Road. Other parts fell at scattered points from the lawns of Buckingham Palace to the Stag Brewery. The British pilot landed uninjured in Hugh Street; but there he met further trouble in a dangerous minute when people on the street thought him to be a German pilot. The German, however, was dead. His body, with field-grey trousers and a sergeant's chevrons, had crashed on to the roof of Nobel House in Buckingham Gate; he had one bullet wound in his right arm.

The dead pilot had attacked Buckingham Palace, laying two un-exploded or time-bombs, one on the lawn and the second in the Regency bathroom overlooking the West Terrace. It was the third time in this the first week that the Palace and the Palace precincts had been hit. In any history of the Londoner's resistance to bombing these in-cidents are of importance. It will be remembered that for London as a whole the week knew three main developments—the very severe damage suffered in the East End, the experience of nightlong raids instead of the short daylight attacks that had been expected, and the heartening music of the barrage that went up on the Wednesday night. To these three may be added the bombing of Buckingham Palace. It has already been said that this was less fortunate for the Luftwaffe than for England. The reason is twofold. It lies in the division that seemed to lie in those days between the East and the West End; and in the tradition of the King as father of his people. In the first few days many of the East Enders thought that they the working people were to bear the brunt of bombardment. Whole rows of their small houses crumbled easily under high explosive blast; for days they went about stupefied, dazed, punch-drunk; through their stupor they felt that across on the other side of London lay a charmed pleasure ground equipped not only with relative immunity but also with great houses of steel and stone that would well withstand the blows that shattered theirs so easily. To an extent, they were right. They *were* bearing the brunt, there *were* safer houses in the west. But they were wrong in be-lieving that the West was to lead a charmed life. And it was this early bombing of Buckingham Palace, and the knowledge that the persons of the King himself and of his Queen were endangered, that shattered their early myth of the suffering poor and the inviolable rich and pre-vented what might have been a strong disaffection emerging from those dazed, terrible days in Dockland. So, by dint of a few ill-chosen bombs, the Luftwaffe had managed to weld the people of London more strongly together than ever before. They became one body of people exposed in their front line. With them, equally exposed, stood their symbolic leader and King. It was known, too, that the King did not remain in Buckingham Palace. He drove through raids in a car that was even smaller and less defended than the people's own small houses. That was enough.

It might be apposite here to study the bombing of Buckingham Palace as a whole, to cheat the strict chronological narrative and go forward in time to examine the overall effects of the war. Up to this time, the Sunday morning of the 15th September, the Palace had received the weight of five bombs, the delayed action bomb that had wrecked the front railings, the three small explosives in the quadrangle and chapel, and an earlier unexploded bomb that fell on the corner of the swimming-pool, situated on the West Terrace. This first bomb had proved awkward. It crashed through the side of the bath, shattering the green tiles, and burying itself beneath. This happened on the early morning of the 9th. Royal Engineers dug throughout the next day in a vain effort to extricate it; but it was a difficult job, they had to leave it—and, fortunately well-buried by the momentum of its own impact, the bomb exploded at half-past one on the morning of the 10th. The side of the swimming-bath was wrecked, some blast was done to windows on the terrace, but no more severe damage than this.

The small unexploded 50 kilo bomb that fell on the 15th made its hole in the ceiling of the Regency bathroom and came to rest on the green carpet alongside the bath. The room with its satined wallpaper and marble fireplace formed part of the Belgian Suite, a residence for foreign guests. It was unoccupied at the time. One of the Palace servants reported the bomb. An officer of the Royal Engineers arrived. He took it up on his shoulder, and carried it over the green carpet, out through the french windows, on to the stone terrace and thence to the lawn, where he dumped it temporarily under a tree. One can visualize the atmosphere at that time—the Foreman taking his Sunday dinner somewhere in the huge basement, the servant bursting in with the news of the bomb, the chase out along the stone-flagged basement corridors with their chocolate and cream walls, up the servants' stairs, on through red-baized connecting doors—then the sight of the bomb innocently asleep by the bath and the impassive reserve of that high-ceilinged room as later the officer removed his strange burden through elegant windows on to the quiet and stately terrace. Still later on that Sunday afternoon this and the other bomb were taken by lorry down to the lake and there exploded.

The next damage was suffered on November 1st, when a high explosive fell on the lawn about forty yards from the west front of the Palace. Windows on this front and the roof-lights of the Riding School were smashed. The behaviour of one piece of splinter from this bomb is interesting, both from the Palace's and the general point of view. This fragment of a Krupp canister must have singed across the air above the close-cropped turf of the lawn, passed just over the stone balustrade of the terrace and in between two decorative stone urns, smashed through the general blast of the window and thence across a ground-floor bedroom—the Spanish Room—to cut a clean hole in the mirror of a large wardrobe, to cut another through the back of the wardrobe and finally to disappear in a small hole of its own making deep into the wall behind. That was the passage of one splinter, having travelled already a distance of about fifty yards. At the time this bedroom was unoccupied. Later on it became the bedroom used by the King himself.

There were further incidents, but none for a time of importance to the main Palace building. A number of incendiaries fell, but the Palace fire brigade and others dealt with these. An anti-aircraft shell exploded in the Mews and damaged some of the royal cars: a few days later high explosive blasted the official quarters within the western wall of the grounds.

But on the 8th March, a Saturday night and brightly moonlit, further direct hits were sustained. A single bomb fell early in the night and destroyed the North Lodge. A policeman on patrol in the forecourt was buried—he must have taken temporary shelter in the doorway of the Lodge as the activity overhead increased. He was found buried to the waist in heavy debris. Rescuers worked hard to extricate him, at last they succeeded—but the constable died as he was being taken by stretcher across the forecourt.

The debris was heavy. Massive cast-iron columns designed by Nash had been hurled to the ground; one huge fragment of stone was thought for a time to be an unexploded parachute mine; rescue work was carried on in dangerous circumstances—for above, dislodged and rickety, there rested a heavy stone entablature surmounted by stone-carved arms and the royal lion and unicorn.

Some time later that same night a stick of seven high explosives fell in a line across the grass of Queen's Gardens, the forecourt of the Palace, and up in a north-westerly direction to Constitution Hill and the Green Park. Blast damage to the front of the Palace, but not severe.

Finally, in June and July 1944, two flying-bombs fell near, affecting only the wall by Constitution Hill and the grounds. The blast of the

June flying-bomb destroyed a summer house of some interest—a wooden white-painted edifice whose roof was supported by four bearded male caryatids evocative of the sea and of figureheads; its design had been attributed to William Kent, and when it was first built in 1730 it rested in the gardens of the Admiralty. But no more than this lonely white summer house in the great park felt the sting of the flying-bomb, only a few windows in the distant Palace suffered blast.

Those then were the incidents at Buckingham Palace—adding up in the main to a demolished lodge, a broken chapel and the smashed end of an outside swimming-bath. Considering its extent, and the number of bombs in its near vicinity, the Palace itself survived the war well. But, as in all other buildings, a raggedness began to show as the days wore on. Glass was out of the windows, and in its place appeared grey boarding that gave the great façades an empty look, as though blinds had been drawn for some endless summer vacation. A section of the tall front railings was replaced by a series of smaller temporary shafts. The high ivied brick wall skirting Constitution Hill became breached with corrugated iron. In the daily life of the forecourt there was no longer the scarlet changing of the guard. Conical armoured sentry-boxes stood by the gates, and Bren-gun carriers rumbled out of William IV's grey Wellington Barracks nearby. The great Portland stone front stood impassive and unbreached, watching with blind eyes an urgent coming and going of cars, the arrivals for audience or investiture, the sudden worming up of clay and the steel-helmeted rescue squads, the sandbags, the khaki soldiers. Within, behind the 1913 façade, around the old forecourt with its ceremonial entrance, there hovered along crimson-carpeted corridors a familiar breath of A.R.P.—for the Palace had its own internal organization—and below in the great basements shelters were built and rooms reinforced with steel girders. This Palace felt itself, and rightly, the object of special bombardment. Its halls and corridors—so often written of as 'gloomy' but really cheerfully coloured and of a fine, well-kept air—knew the incursions of blast, of flying glass and the tearing down of plaster.

At Marble Arch on the 17th September there occurred a grave disaster. One bomb—and only a small one—pierced the roadway above the underground subway and there exploded. This had been considered one of the safest places of shelter in the City. The subway had been built in great strength, girders and concrete massed the roof to take the weight of heavy traffic passing round the Arch above. Apparently only the nose-cap penetrated—it made a minute hole and must have pierced between two closely-knit girders. It was the unlucky chance. The subway was filled with shelterers—some squatting and sleeping, others who had come down for a moment off the streets. So that in effect the small explosive burst in amongst the people like a heavy grenade, flew along the tunnel ripping the white tiles off as it burst and sucked its way through. When wardens and stretcher and rescue parties arrived, they were faced with a terrible scene. The dead had been killed by blast— there was hardly a scratch on them, though in every case their clothes had been ripped off. But apart from the bursting of the bomb the sharp tiles had had a lacerating effect, flying swiftly and causing more casualties than there might otherwise have been. This happened only ten days after the beginning of Westminster's Blitz, and for many of the A.R.P. personnel it was their first experience of death and wounding on such a scale. There were forty known casualties, of whom over twenty were dead.[1] The shocked in that concentration of shelterers amounted to many more. It was a bewildering, dreadful time; and it is remembered at the Report Centre that when one rescue leader, a strong man and a good worker, telephoned his message—through his words he was sobbing. It is remembered, too, that one part-time warden who happened to be near—an unknown man and off duty—worked on the site all night. He could never afterwards be traced. This gratuitous work was indicative of what was afterwards often to happen throughout the raiding periods. Men and women off duty very often spent their rest-nights out again on the job. It is an understandable human impulse to give every help at such times; and those were times when it often satisfied the nerves to be out and active rather than to be waiting and listening at home; and yet—it must be remembered that such action on the part of an A.R.P. worker often succeeded a night of exhausting work, perhaps in the winter as long as fifteen or more hours on the job, and that sleep for that rest-night would have been easy, and necessary, and entitled, and in conscience earned.

On that and the following nights an anti-aircraft shell exploded by the west door of St. Margaret's, there was a fire at Taylor's Depository in Pimlico, and bombs struck notably the Record Office in Chancery Lane, Charing Cross Station, the grounds of Westminster Cathedral, Whitehall outside the Scottish Office; and, ominously, the first parachute mine to affect Westminster fell on the Lambeth side of the river,

[1] It must be noted here that these and all other casualty figures mentioned throughout this account are taken from the City Council's internal records. It is possible that on occasions further casualties were transported away from the bombsite to outside areas and never accurately reported. However, it is not likely that these would have varied much from the figures given here. The proportions of the incidents can be fairly assumed.

blasting across the Thames windows in the War Office and in Scotland Yard.

The bomb that fell on the pavement outside the Scottish Office was of the delayed action type. It was realized that when it exploded serious damage would be caused not only to the Scottish Office itself, but also to the Banqueting Hall of Whitehall Palace—the fine building designed for James I by Inigo Jones and now used as the United Services Museum. Two officers of the Rescue Service volunteered to build a sandbag wall round the bomb. Traffic was diverted. The wall was built in part—and then with the minutes ticking away, it was found that there were not enough sandbags. So the building had to pause. The men went to fetch more and very much by chance they escaped death—for the bomb exploded when they were away down the street. However, their efforts were rewarded when the damage of the explosion came to be assessed. The wall had been built just high enough to deflect the blast upwards. Thus the Scottish Office sustained only slight injury. The Banqueting Hall escaped unharmed.

On the night of the 22nd September there occurred a grave tragedy at the large block of flats by the river known as Dolphin Square. Up to the time of this incident, it had been an active night. Several bombs had fallen in the Pimlico district, and already there had been evacuations. The Heavy Rescue Service stationed nearby had been evacuated to the main A.R.P. depot in Dolphin Square, and another unexploded bomb had brought in a number of people for temporary shelter in the basement under a wing called Hawkins House. During this time there was much gunfire, and the sound of many bombs—the night was alive. One bomb across the river had struck a gasworks, breaking some steam valves and setting up from this wreckage a piercing shriek ceaseless and on one monotonous edged note, a merciless and nerve-racking sound that continued for three-quarters of an hour. Then it stopped. There was peace—relative peace. Until some time after eleven the unlucky bomb came, the bomb that drove in obliquely piercing the side of Hawkins House just above the ground, blowing in the concrete retaining wall and exploding in the shelter. It was the shelter filled with the evacuated.

As though mobilized for the tragedy, there was exactly on the spot a depot full of A.R.P. personnel with the added strength of the previously evacuated Rescue Service. These massed rescuers were thus at the dark, disrupted shelter within seconds. They found by the light of their torches a dismal and terrible scene. Among the wreckage, the pieces of torn concrete, there appeared a wall of clay. From this, muffled, the buried and wounded screamed. Clay, earth, darkness. Gas was escaping. There was only one approach—through one narrow passage. Torches only could be used. And so by these hurried fitful beams, and into the wet clinging clay, they began to dig.

In twenty-eight minutes fifty-eight people were taken away down the narrow passage. There were as many as eight squads of stretcher-bearers working. The CO_2 fumes hung densely, so thick that rescuers were lightly gassed and staggered as they took away their stretchers. Over in the depot, in the underground garage, the First Aid Post was filled. Doctors and nurses were faced there not with the light wounds for which the post was equipped—but with serious and dreadful injuries. The work was heavy and continued throughout the night. . . .

It was a grave instance of multiple injury. It showed again that it was not necessarily the strength of the high explosive that caused the greatest destruction, but rather the place and the structure into which by chance it fell. And there is one more aspect of the incident which must be remembered—that these people who were killed and injured had already been subjected to one direct hit that night. To be hit, to be injured once is bad enough; but part of the hardness of the experience of being bombed is that a knock-out blow does not decide the issue—a person already homeless, wounded, down, may be burnt, blasted, buried again and again. There is no immediate rear line. The first moments of calm after evacuation may be brutally shattered, as at Hawkins House; the first moment of rest between the clean hospital sheets may see those sheets burst into incendiary flame; the first moments of true consciousness after twenty-four hours wedged and smothered and trapped in debris may awake to the sounding again of the sirens and the first far rumbling of guns.

It was, as has been said, not necessarily the strength of a high explosive that caused the greatest damage; but until then Westminster had not experienced an exception—the parachute mine. One fell the next night in Savile Row—opposite the new Central Police Station.

This building was a departure from the typical police station. It was constructed of stone on a steel framework, decorated in a style that might have suggested the offices of a business concern. It was well equipped with anti-gas arrangements, emergency lighting, protected communications: but it was weak in one respect—there was much interior glass partitioning. So that when Westminster's first parachute mine came to earth in Savile Row just before ten that night, all this glass partitioning was shattered by the terrific mine-blast, whose explosive force is not at all muffled by penetration into the earth but spreads wide from the first impact. The building stood up to the blast —but the glass partitions caused much cutting and wounding. Though casualties were many, both inside the station and out in suddenly shattered Savile Row, there was one mercy—a number of the police due for night relief were just at that moment parading in the basement, and were thus saved and available to assist in rescue work.

That same night St. Anne's Church in Soho was for the first time damaged; also the Queen's Theatre in Shaftesbury Avenue. Then on the 26th an incident occurred which demands note—an exploded and an unexploded bomb fell at the junction of Denbigh Street and Belgrave Road. The damage done was not unusual for such nights. Similar bombs had fallen without number in those first weeks. As it was, people were reported trapped in a vault shelter beneath the pavement. Water was pouring in from broken mains. It was feared that all those trapped would be drowned. Rescue work was made doubly dangerous by the discovery of a second unexploded bomb lying close by. To complicate matters, a gas main had been set alight. Gas engineers were called. The Auxiliary Fire Service were summoned both to restrict the fire and pump water out of the flooded basements beneath. Under those conditions, and always with the menace of further bombs overhead, rescue work went on through the night. Bodies were recovered from the water. It was found later that they had not been drowned, they were killed by the bomb.

Then, at a quarter to nine the next morning, the officer in charge of Westminster stretcher parties went over to inspect the gas-filled crater of the bomb diagnosed as unexploded. At that moment it exploded. The officer received injuries to his head from which he died.

This man died in an attempt to save others. His death stands as a monument not only to his own courage but to the sacrifice of all those who undertook the dangerous task of identifying these bombs of delayed action, and who were themselves no less courageous—perhaps just luckier. In those days talk among rescue officers and others who volunteered for this task was full of such phrases as: 'Its fin—about three inches under the pavement.' Or: 'Couldn't see it for clay—mucky job.' There was a clinical, and at times jocular indifference in their very objective attitude towards this job. Sometimes, in the perverse way in which such feelings developed, they argued as to whose bomb it was. They searched among impossible debris in much the same way as a golfer might search for a ball lost in the rough—with some impatience, some anger, but a determination to succeed. One man, on finding his bomb, used always to roll it over, spit on his finger, and with this rub away the dust and mud that caked the German maker's name. One of such men, indifferent to his own safety in the interest of the safety of others, died on that morning of the 26th September.

On the next night the Houses of Parliament suffered their first widespread hurt, when a bomb fell in Old Palace Yard. However, the damage hardly affected the structure, it was extensive only in that so many windows on the west front of the House of Lords were blasted from their gothic encasement, and that the stone tracery of one of the huge hall-size windows was shattered. Glass in Westminster Abbey was also blown out; Home Guards stationed in Westminster Hall were blown over; and the raised sword of the dark equestrian statue of Richard Cœur de Lion was bent—but never lowered.

This night was followed by a sharp morning raid, in which bombs were dropped mostly in the Victoria and Pimlico districts. Among other places Chelsea Barracks was badly hit, with many military casualties. On the 28th the East Wing of Somerset House was struck by high explosives, and on the following night three 500 kilo bombs fell in the quadrangle of the War Office in Whitehall. Fortunately not much damage was sustained here; one of the bombs was broken on impact with girders within the building, spilling its explosive mixture. This was one of the cases of a gas scare—the explosive mixture came into contact with water and there evolved a suspicious fuming that smelt like gas and brought the order, in the muddled dark night, for gas-masks.

These, with one small unexploded bomb in South Moulton Street, were the only two incidents recorded for those two nights. The weight of bombs was dwindling, and on the following nights very little occurred —a few scattered high explosives, a few oil bombs, some anti-aircraft shells—until on the night of the 3rd October there dropped nothing heavier than a shell. The activity overhead continued, the sirens hurried London to its shelters, damage was suffered elsewhere—but Westminster itself had in terms of destruction, if not of apprehension, a respite during four nights.

The bombing had lasted nearly a month. Up to that time, no town in the world had undergone a similar experience. Educated as we now are towards the idea of 2,000 bomber raids, of the enormous weights of American and British bombs dropped on Axis cities, and later with the obscenity of the atom bomb—now these raids of 50 to 300 bombers with their smaller bombs seem insignificant in the fiercer light of contemporary explosion. But *then*—and this must continually be stressed

—nothing like it had been known. Warsaw, Rotterdam and others had suffered dreadful destruction—but not on the continuous scale of London's experience.

After a month Londoners recovered from the initial surprise and shock, and knew themselves to be in what amounted to a state of siege. It seemed impossible that it could go on, it seemed improbable that it would stop. People became inured to a new kind of life. The habits and the face of the town were changing. There was in people's minds a day-to-day facing of a real situation—yet behind this still a dream-like incredulity. After so many years—Britain invested? Britain alone? Without allies? Britain to be invaded by a German army and the har-nessed wealth of Europe? There was little light. The radiance, perhaps, of a determination to fight it out; but in many minds no concrete hope. However, the actual bombing gave little time for speculation. There was enough action on the doorstep. Out in the wide world of the war Quis-ling had assumed power in Norway, the Italians were on the move for-ward beyond Sidi Barrani, Germany was extending its power in Rumania, ominously Hitler met Mussolini on the Brenner; against this, there shone the bright light of our air victories over England—185 German planes destroyed on 15th September, 133 on the 27th; and there was the moralizing effect of the first heavy R.A.F. raid on Berlin, the arrival in Britain of American destroyers and several successful naval engagements. But every night in the dark small world of London's intimate streets these matters receded, and under the urging drone of the bombers, the weaving searchlights, the thunder of bombs and the crack of guns the moments became vivid and active, each episode of gigantic proportion, like a shadow that suddenly lengthens on the wall. Hot, cold, sharp, slow moments of intense being; moments that then extended themselves into hours, that brought with them the ex-haustions of cold and sleeplessness, so that the total experience is most remembered as a curious double exposure of tensity and dullness.

The weather continued warm, but the nights were lengthening. People looked forward to the winter and the long cold darkness with no relish. The streets emptied now after dusk, and the blackout became largely the property of the wardens and police; though in the West End there persisted a dogged and darkly hurrying crowd of revellers. A City bereft of electric and neon light took on a new beauty—by moonlight the great buildings assumed a remote and classic magnifi-cence, cold, ancient, lunar palaces carved in bone from the moon; and angular overdressed Victorian eccentricities were purified, un-coloured, quietened by the moon's ubiquitous sanity. But on clouded nights and moonless nights it was not so beautiful—in the total black-out nothing could be seen. Torchlight was rationed by a filter of paper, the insides of passing buses glimmered blue, cigarette ends became the means of demonstrating one's passage. A match might not be struck, nor a headlight switched on. A glimmer of 'starlight' filtered down from some street-lamps in the main thoroughfares, the red, green and yellow traffic lights were masked to show only thin crosses of their colour. This darkness flared into sudden relief—in the yellow flash of gunfire, in the whitish-green hiss of incendiaries, in the copper-red reflection of the fires, in the yellow flare of the burning gas main, in the red explosion of the bomb. In such light the gilt tracery of Big Ben's tower flashed into colour, the sombre drab alleys round Covent Garden blazed with a theatrical daylight, the corrugated skylines of Park Lane and Knights-bridge showed black against the deep red sky, the streets of Pimlico and Soho saw the high scarfing columns of a naked gas flame flaring like some giant idealization of the naphtha flames that through the years had lit their fairs and their stalls.

These were the lights—but there were also dark streets, streets where suddenly a house of blackness collapsed with a roar, shifting down heavily like some bricked elephant lumbering to its knees, thickening the darkness with a poisonous cloud of dust, shrouding the moment after its fall with a fearful empty silence broken only by small sounds, the whispering of broken water pipes, slight shiftings of debris, moans and little cries of the injured; then into the torchlight of the wardens there would stagger those untrapped, lonely figures in the dust-fog bleached grey with powder and streaked and patched with black blood; or—there would be nobody, and not a sound, only a living silence in the knowledge that under a smoking, spawning mass of timber and brick and dust there lay pressed and stifled the bodies of warm people whose minutes were slowly ticking away, whose rescue was absurdly blocked by a mass of intractible weight that angered those standing so few yards above. These are not pleasant memories, but they must be written—otherwise the picture that was essentially one of dirt and anguish be-comes too clean. Death and wounding from such explosives was never as neat as a bullet in the head; but the details shall be left to a Barbusse. One of the few consolations was that the explosive force proved in most cases so great as to shock its victim into unconsciousness or at least into a physical incomprehension of what had occurred.

So after one of these sudden rifts in the City's streets, there would come a solitary running figure rounding the corners and racing down the blacked-out pavement—a warden getting the first news to his Post.

From the downstairs room in the Post the call would be telephoned to the Report Centre at City Hall, and thence out to one of Westminster's four depots, the great subterranean concentrations where ambulances, stretcher parties, heavy rescue parties and other mobile aid services were waiting with the engines of their vehicles tuned up and their personnel at the ready. A few minutes later those streets, alternatively echoing alive with noise and as suddenly setting gelid in a graveyard silence, would resound to the crescendo of approaching engines and the bells of the ambulances. As they braked to a stop by the bombed house, other vehicles might be heard travelling in other directions in other streets, fire-bells ringing, the staccato groan of a hooter, a strangely resonant purr of tyres and the scream of cornering brakes. There was a feeling of mad pursuit in so many ant-like directions as the forces of defence followed the direction of their different orders; the bombing at this period was scattered, muddled, a maze of incidents everywhere —it set a far greater burden on the mobilization of resources than did, say, the more compact yet more extensive damage done by the flying-bombs some years later. But through those nights they worked with other bombs falling around, with sometimes the fire hoses making a cold saturation of their limited world of rubble and dirt and death, with fire itself breaking out, with gas escaping, with ton-weight walls crumbling, with the ever-present and ever-nauseous stenches of disintegration sickening the air, the smells of charred wood, pulverized plaster, old brick, mortar, all the mouldering quiet of years broken loose in one sharp moment.

Much was learnt in those first weeks. The problem of unexploded bombs, the discovery that you could kick an incendiary into the gutter and beat it out with a chair, the strength of the parachute mine. On the whole, the bombs had been small ones—a majority of 50 kilo high explosives were dropped in that period. There was no panic among the people; this was contrary to all expectation—careful provision had been made against panic, such as the construction of a tower with loud-speakers for directing the crowds that might have been expected in the forecourt of Victoria Station, and such as the setting up of wooden palings with single entrances round groups of street and trench shelters. Whether gas might have caused a panic is still doubtful, but on the whole people reacted well, extraordinarily well. There was much private fear—it was seldom made public, never became infectious on any large scale. At that time, morale was as high as at any time during the war. Britain was standing against the heaviest military machine ever known. Yet, though no sensible notion of success presented itself, the people seemed charged with extraordinary hope. The successes of the Battle of Britain in the air had much to do with this. There had also been the Churchill speeches in which blood and toil and tears had been offered, together with a fight to the death on the beaches and on the most inland hill. 'All right' was the response; it was the moment to be stimulated, the time of inaction had passed, there remained to be done some solid work of no half measure. At the same time, the bombing was no less terrifying, and shelters were used. It would have been absurd not to have used them—every casualty was a weight on the civic resources. However, this became a most individual matter and the tale of sheltering was not as it had been envisaged.

Although in the first few nights the street shelters and the trenches were packed, they became the least popular as time went on. One of the strongest tendencies was to get deep down, and a few nights after the bombing began vast crowds invaded the tube stations. They lay anywhere. In rows like huddled fish they lay on the platforms. They slept in the passages and on the escalators. Women, children, men, suitcases, blankets, pillows, rugs, coats and even sheets lay packed in a solid mass. The trains came and went, the people tried to sleep and slept. And trains would push the hot air from the last station in front of them so that the temperature in some of these packed stations rose very high, as high as 90 degrees. Such temperatures caused high winds in the passages; perhaps the windiest corner in London was the escalator bottom at Piccadilly, where one old gentleman pitched himself every evening at five o'clock. In these winds one saw such improvisations as a string contrivance lashing down the bedclothes and the pillow so that they would not blow away. An idea of the number of shelterers may be gathered from the case of the Piccadilly Circus Station—4,000 on a peak night. As time went on the transport authorities and wardens instituted a special ticket system regulating the number of shelterers—though this number was kept at an absolute maximum.

Other main shelter preferences were for those situated in the basements of the heavier buildings, or those in the vaults beneath the pavement—conveniently beneath the front door. Later, vast improvements were to be made for comfort and health in all these shelters—but in the first weeks life was still muddled, makeshift; the enemy's intention was not then clear, and priority of thought had to go to the equipment of a new army and the factories to feed it. At that time, unknown to the shelterers, there were in Britain only fifty tanks. Police were commandeering obsolete rifles from theatrical stores. The Home Guard were issued with pikes.

Westminster, of course, was unlike a purely residential district. In the office and shopping regions where a huge daytime population lived, there was comparative emptiness at night. In compensation crowds arrived from the east and from the south. There was once a difficult time in the strong underground shelters beneath Thames House. Here thousands came from across Lambeth Bridge. Their invasion was understandable, they had been bombed heavily in their smaller houses and they must have watched the concrete skyline across the river with envy and plain criticism. But large as it was, Thames House could not accommodate a limitless flow. People were admitted, in hundreds; but serious overcrowding ensued, the temperature rose dangerously, and the Westminster City Engineer had to rush down heavy emergency fans which were built into the wall within twenty-four hours—a notable achievement.

This first September gave birth to a phrase familiar to the times: 'London Can Take It.' Whether London's attitude was exceptional is a controversial point. Madrid took it, Chungking took it, Leningrad took it. London did, too. The question is asked, 'And what else could they have done? What other course was open?' The answer is that the people could have rioted; they could have left their jobs and evacuated themselves in disorderly millions to the country; the personnel of the A.R.P. organizations could have left the streets and taken shelter; and generally, if such extreme disorders had not occurred, then the will to work could have slackened and workers could have excused themselves and stayed at home or in shelters. None of these courses would necessarily have had their decisive effect on the war; but each of them in various degrees would have placed heavy burdens on the running of an already strained national machine—and vitally they would have lowered the value of Britain's diamond asset, the spiritual wealth of a high morale and a great will to win.

However, none of these courses were taken. London stood firm. The real story of this resistance is not the plain fact that the bombing was endured, but the extraordinary degree of normalcy which was maintained. It would have been so simple then just not to have turned up for one's job in the morning after the raid. But the opposite happened. The workers did turn up, although it meant being late, although trains were dislocated, although it meant in some cases walking ten or more miles, although sometimes the front door of the home they left for work might have disappeared in the night, although they had had no sleep and no breakfast and had spent the night out with the blood of their less fortunate neighbours. And this went on night after night, with little respite, with only the colder weather ahead and the longer darkness and the longer raids. The effort was considerable. It must always be remembered that it was voluntary. There were plenty of excuses to hand. The simple fact remained that these excuses were not made. The stubborn individual will merged into a grim, effective communal will— from the free lifts advertised in all cars to the old lady with a saucepan for a tin helmet who handed out her tea in the fire-glow of splintered streets. The faint-hearted were few. There was a bit of grousing—but that was concerned more with a spoilt breakfast than a ruined home; the ruined home was accepted, angrily, grimly. Otherwise there were jokes, those ironical and impudent understatements so much the property of the cockney.

But the narrative of events must be resumed. The general picture may be summarized later—at the end of the period called 'The Old Blitz'. For though these first nights were the most surprising, they were by no means all. Much worse was to come, and the experience of Westminster itself was to become much sharper. In passing one further note must be made, note of the courage of women; women faced the tasks in the street and the long ardours of apprehension every bit as well as the men, and by doing so inspired men to greater efforts. It is taken for granted that anything written about Civil Defence is no story of male enterprise; women took the burden equally, obviously not in work beyond their material muscle, but in every exposure out on the pavements—like the auxiliary firewomen who drove petrol wagons through flaming streets and women wardens who shouldered that most vulnerable job alongside the man.

On the 7th October, after four nights of much aerial activity but in Westminster no damage, the Luftwaffe struck again. At a quarter to eight the Fire Station in Shaftesbury Avenue received a direct hit. Firemen were killed and injured—and in the official record book there is a note descriptive perhaps in its shortness and its blunt pathos of much of the inconsequential tragedy of those nights: 'Two dead pedestrians.' It often happened. It was not unusual. Two people who by chance were walking then along the street—from their job? Or to dinner? On their way to further work? Two people who paused to shelter a moment in the doors of the Fire Station. The bomb chose that particular place, they were killed. People above in the same building came sliding down on the debris, shocked and bruised, but unhurt and able to walk the next day.

Structurally, little remained of the Fire Station but a packed mass of debris. On the same night, No. 145 Piccadilly was hit. This large stone-faced house looking out over the Wellington Arch had been the residence of the King and Queen when Duke and Duchess of York. At the time, it was being used as the headquarters of a relief and comforts fund. The main damage was caused inside the building, but its grey façade became another of the dark, empty-windowed screens that were forming a cumulative scar on the tattering face of London streets. By the light of the next day, while these wreckages were being assessed, at ten minutes to nine, more bombs were dropped. It seems that fighter bombers flew in fast; from their short stab there resulted a most unlucky series of events. A stick of bombs fell in a line with Charing Cross Station and Whitehall Place. Both the Underground Railway and the Southern Railway stations suffered, together with the Paymaster General's Office in Whitehall, old buildings at the rear of the Ministry of Agriculture and Fisheries in Whitehall Place, the War Office and Somerset House.

The Charing Cross group of stations received three bombs. There were forty-eight known casualties, of whom eight were dead. One bomb fell on the line over the north footway of Victoria Embankment; a signal box and wires were damaged. More seriously, the second bomb dropped through the roof of the main Southern Railway station over a main line platform, bringing down heavy debris and causing casualties. One carriage of a loaded train was hit badly, the orderly platforms were transformed in a second into a hall of chaos. Kiosks were blown over on their sides among a general disruption of railway apparatus and stacked goods. Peculiarly, there seemed to be ice-cream cartons everywhere. And while people staggered dazed on these main platforms, a further stratum of the chaos had developed in the underground station below. A third bomb had crashed through the glass dome above the District Railway platforms and had exploded on the line. Four people were killed. Many more missed death by good fortune, for a minute earlier a train packed with office-workers had left that very platform. As it was, the bomb fell by the down line platform—curiously injuring few on that side, for the cut of the platform tended to divert the blast upwards; it was therefore the people on the far platform who suffered most.

That these bombs fell before nine and not a quarter of an hour later was fortunate; for the Paymaster General's Office in Whitehall was severely hit and by that time few people had arrived at their desks. Nine o'clock was the dividing mark. And at this time the night-staff who would normally have been on duty were somewhere else having breakfast and washing. As it was, two people were killed. But over at

No. 5 Whitehall Place casualties were heavier—six dead and 20 wounded. This was yet another case of old buildings being simply pulverized by the bomb's force. The more substantial Somerset House and War Office building stood up better. But in the east wing of Somerset House five were killed. And in the War Office, where two bombs fell in the quadrangle, there were some ten casualties. One of these latter bombs broke, but the missing detonator caused much trouble, isolating the room in which it lay. The bomb that did not break penetrated through the quadrangle surface and demolished a new luncheon club that had only just been opened; among other things a refrigerator was damaged, and from this ammonia leaked and caused a gas warning to be sounded.

Bombs continued to fall through the next nights. An outstanding incident occurred on the 11th; it may illustrate the difficulties and unusual conditions under which A.R.P. services were often called to work. The bomb—a heavy calibre high explosive—fell at about eight o'clock at Laundry Yard near the site of two disused gas-holder excavations. It was a pitch-black night. Two old empty houses nearby were demolished, and from these there issued a dense fog of dust that hung over the area, obscuring the dark further and gritting the air with lime. Rescuers arrived to find that the bomb had lifted the roof of a surface shelter in which nine people were taking refuge. They were safe, shocked but unhurt. However, it so happened that at this particular hour the shifts were changing at the adjoining premises of the Gas Light and Coke Company, and this and the bad visibility of only a few yards made it difficult to know how many street casualties there might be. Timekeepers' huts and other outbuildings had been shifted and demolished. For a while wardens and rescue parties, wearing handkerchiefs over their mouths against the lime-fog, searched blindly. Then it was found that men had been blown into the site of one of the gasholders. In the blackness, wardens descended by ladder.

The depth was thirty-five feet. At the bottom, they found six foot of water. But the flooring was concave, so that towards the centre it rose clear of the water. On that dark space of dry land two men were found badly injured. Heavy wooden beams had been blown down on them. Rescue parties above rigged up tackle, those below bridged the water. The two men, still conscious, were hoisted up. As they were carried away on stretchers, in the fog and the confusion and with the life ebbing from them, they had the guts to sing and to joke. Later both were to die in hospital. And later two of their comrades were found dead in the water at the side of the pit.

On the following night a major disaster occurred at the tube station in Trafalgar Square. It was one of the unluckiest incidents of the Blitz. A heavy bomb fell on the roadway near King Charles I's statue. It penetrated the surface and exploded over the subway of the underground station beneath. By chance, this explosion occurred above the bottom of the escalator, 40 feet below. Concussion drove down, the steel and concrete casing collapsed, and an avalanche of earth was loosed upon the square at the foot of the escalator. Many people were sheltering, they were buried. To make matters worse water from a broken main percolated through the already unstable roofing, bringing down continual falls of earth until there was left a chasm above from which fully seventy tons had fallen.

Rescue workers were faced with a dreadful task. Though some shelterers had managed to escape, many lay crushed and buried in the huge mound of wet, loamy brown earth. These were people who had sought shelter as deep and presumably thus as safe as anywhere in London: but the unlucky chance had come. In the roadway above, there was little to be seen. In fact, one stretcher-party car, loaded with extra bandages and informed that there was on hand a major disaster, arrived at the crater, saw no activity to merit their idea of a large incident, and drove on at full speed to where the reflection of a fire showed from Wardour Street. But again they saw nothing much there—and returned to search again for this disaster of such huge proportion: which they found, underground, deep beneath the innocent square.

Rescue work continued for hours under appalling conditions. Earth was falling continually. As they dug, the cavities they created were filled in with more earth from above. The temperature rose high. Soon they were working stripped to the waist. Transport officials had produced two powerful lamps that were then directed on the ceiling above. Cracks in the earth were seen opening. A warning would be called—then masses of earth crashed down thudding on the dreadful mound piling ever higher. Authorities appealed to the warden in charge to have work stopped until engineers could erect a staging and props to protect the rescue men. There seemed little hope that anyone buried could still be alive. But the rescue party refused to stop work while there was a chance. They worked on, sweating, and dodged the falls until the last of the entombed were released. The bomb had fallen before nine o'clock. Rescue work was completed before midnight.

At this incident there were in all forty known casualties, of whom seven were dead. Away from the central point of digging, stretchers were manœuvred awkwardly up the long escalator with the injured strapped on. A first aid party in charge of a doctor attended to slight injuries or shock in a train pulled up at one of the platforms nearby. And in the tunnels around many shelterers, reassured and in ignorance of the true nature of the disaster, continued their night's sleep.

On that same night five more heavy explosives fell on the much hit War Office building. This time the roof and top two floors of one side wing were destroyed. Later, valuable printing machinery was ruined by a fall of coping stone. But again the damage was not as severe as it might have been; and to all intents and purposes, viewing it from Whitehall, the building might never have been hit.

Another bomb fell in the centre of the National Gallery. Debris was scattered, and serious flooding in the basement endangered valuable paintings stored there. Raiding continued nightly, but as from a week before—on the 5th October—the Germans had ceased to send over heavy bombers by day. In daylight there were more short warnings caused by fighter bombers; though no incidents are recorded in Westminster. On the night of the 14th October the area was more sharply hit than for some time. Church House received a direct high explosive, and this was the night of the bombing of St. James's Church in Piccadilly, of the Carlton club, of the Treasury Garden (with blast damage to Downing Street) of a large fire in the Fifty Shilling Tailor's building in Piccadilly—besides many serious incidents in other parts of the City.

St. James's Church was hit early in the raid. The bomb transformed the stately line of Wren's roof into what appeared in the firelight like a chopped sea of frozen slate. The tower stood, but in the rectory there was trouble—the bomb had trapped people underneath in the kitchen. There were other casualties, too, and very heavy stone blocks impeded rescue efforts. The Church itself was on fire, Piccadilly was blocked by a large crater, the building opposite—the Fifty Shilling Tailor's premises —was ablaze. From the upper windows, wax dummies were seen dropping down into the road like blazing corpses. The ring of rooftops round Piccadilly Circus was alight with incendiaries—like a ring of candles for a Roman triumph.

Down by the Rectory rescue work began. Bombs were still falling, flames from surrounding buildings threw out a fierce light. Operations proceeded at first slowly. Passers-by helped throw out the fringe of loose rubble. But heavy paving stones obstructed progress, and in those days the Rescue Service was not equipped with machinery to cut quickly through such obstacles. However, a compressor, used for cutting up the road, happened to be standing nearby. The rescue workers commandeered it, and with the help of a soldier started drilling the stone at speed. But to reach those trapped in the central inner debris was even more difficult—it took in the end twelve hours, and to complete the task they had to burrow, underneath rubble, through two walls still firm in the ruins and after that through a third wall three feet thick before they reached the kitchen. One of those within was brought out alive—but died later.

At the Carlton Club in Pall Mall a bomb crashed through the roof and exploded in the Library. This was situated just above the dining hall where many people were at dinner. They escaped, though the upper part of the club itself was blown hollow. A soldier passing outside was not so fortunate—he was killed by the unlucky chance of a falling lamp-post. A car was parked by the steps—and one of the huge lumps of masonry from the upper cornices of the great club building fell through the roof; the car was empty—but this may illustrate part of the character of bombing, where danger did not only result from the bomb's explosion and the immediate debris, but from huge weights and sharp splinters flying outside the perimeter of expected death.

Along Pall Mall incendiaries were dropping. It is worth remembering another passer-by who helped during this raid, in a way smaller but none the less indicative of the feeling of the times. She was a young woman in evening dress. Incendiaries fell on the pavement at her feet. Without thought for how those feet of hers were clad—in light evening shoes—she began kicking the fiercely spitting bombs into the gutter. Then she made off to where she could find some earth to smother the bombs—and returned with this slung in her own fine evening cloak over her shoulder.

In Lowndes Street two George medals were earned by wardens engaged in high level rescue work. It is an instance of those rescues that had to be effected not on the ground and underneath, as was mostly the case, but in the upper floors of buildings that might collapse at any moment. In this case, the two wardens climbed up a lead water-pipe attached to a wall damaged and in a very dangerous condition. They searched among the upper debris for one and a half hours in order to discover two persons known to be in the bedrooms. Eventually they found them dead. But there was a third person reported to be there. They continued the search. They found this woman alive on the second floor. She was lowered by knotted sheets found in the wrecked rooms. During all this time raiders were circling overhead and three large bombs exploded nearby, setting ablaze not more than thirty yards away a gas main whose flames leaped to the rooftops of adjoining buildings. It must be remembered that a blazing gas main, or any bright fire, frequently attracted the interest of the bomb-aimers above.

The next night of the 15th October was the heaviest raid that London generally had yet suffered. The enemy used four hundred bombers: Westminster received its quota of their delivery. One of the first high explosives fell in the middle of the underground garage yard of Dolphin Square. It fell through the garden and exploded four yards from the shelter where A.R.P. personnel were waiting for a call-out. In this vast underground room 160 private cars were garaged: sixty were totally destroyed and of the rest only seven remained whole. Fire started, but this was quickly controlled by ambulance personnel with extinguishers. The sensation of chaos in this smoking and wrecked garage, underground and in darkness, and of the night that followed, may be realized from the words of ambulance women who were there at the time: 'Terrific explosion . . . a strong smell of cordite . . . above the wall saw the ceiling lit up at the same time as a dense swirl of dust descended on us . . . I felt as if a huge hand was pinning me down on my bench . . . tried to get through the garage to the far end, where ambulances and pickets were, but found it impossible . . . raced upstairs and through the garden lit up by searchlights and bursting ack-ack shells and flares —to find ambulances intact . . . in the meantime, the garage and shelter were flooded to a depth of nearly a foot, equipment room and offices flattened as by a hurricane, and of course the telephones destroyed . . . one of my drivers had her cotton coat ripped up the back as if by a razor, and she was peppered with glass in her face, arms and back . . . ambulances brought round to the west side of the building—in a couple of hours we were ready to function again.'

With the Superintendent using a telephone in one of the flats, with one of the ramps already blocked by a house-fall from a previous night, with a huge fire blazing in a furniture warehouse two streets away, this microcosm of Dolphin Square continued its night. Bombs continued to fall—one 'curling just like a shooting star, and falling diagonally'—until at half-past one two more explosives hit a corner of the building; but this time there were no casualties, and not much damage, the bombs hitting a coke store and grass near the south-east corner of the building. But at half-past two a further bomb found its mark in this area—killing an ambulance driver on the ramp. Now both ramps were out of action, this second one blocked by girders. By that time others of the ambulances were out—attending to serious casualties—when a parachute mine landed in Alderney and Cambridge Streets. There a stretcher-bearer from Dolphin Square received fatal injuries; he refused to leave a stretcher case when the parachute was in full view coming down.

Thereafter—more calls, more trouble throughout the night. One ambulance reported into the depot 'with a house in the back'; it was, in fact, full of bricks, with holes in the roof and curtains ripped away —for a bomb had blown up a house just as they were on their way home, fortunately empty, from hospital.

The parachute mine at Alderney Street demolished or blasted out of use as many as 150 houses, sending 300 people homeless into the night, injuring seriously about 60 people—and killing 23. This was the first time that rescue workers had been faced with destruction on such a wide scale—it was the first parachute mine to strike a heavily populated area in Westminster and such an area of easily demolished buildings. On arriving at the scene they were met by a vista of desolation that at first seemed to have no end. This was new to men whose experience so far had been at least confined within more or less visible limits. But the destruction caused by a land mine was difficult to believe —and when believed full of foreboding. German bombing was on the acceleration. The bombscape at Alderney Street underlined the future. And for those organizing A.R.P. it underlined the need for some central point of rendezvous for all services, in that here there was a havoc of many incidents centred in one area. But soon a grasp was had on the situation, and throughout the night personnel worked under fire— suffering in all as many as eleven fatal casualties. Fragments isolate themselves in the memory of what was then too vast a field to visualize as a whole—again the smell of explosive mixture, again the heavy dust hovering for hours, again the discovery that many people were shelter- ing in empty houses and basements without informing anyone of their whereabouts. Such people ran the risk of never being found. Or, as happened elsewhere, of being found as many as twelve months later during final demolition work. But rescue workers searched as best they could, as long as their strength availed, and as long as there was informa- tion to suppose that people lay in the under-debris. Of the dead, one man was found in the back kitchen of a house up against the wall and shielding a woman and two children. Another man, buried for as long as twenty-four hours, was still alive—and only because through the packed rubble there had percolated a slow trickle of water from a broken lavatory pipe far above. Wardens there at Alderney Street saw another mine descending while they were working. It came floating down on its parachute—the blank object that high above might be a baled-out airman, but lower can be distinguished as something like a tall blunt-ended pillar-box. This one came down fully illuminated by searchlights, and in a rash of anti-aircraft shells that finally exploded it in the air. One other landed unexploded in the Greycoat School and was later dismantled without harm. A fourth reached its destination alive—and blew off a corner of Leicester Square.

This Leicester Square mine fell towards half-past three, so that there were relatively few people about. It struck the corner building above the old Perroquet restaurant and next door to Thurston's famous billiards house. The Leicester Square Theatre a few yards away suffered only superficial damage, illustrating thus once again how well concrete and steel stood up to those high blasts; but Thurston's was largely wrecked. Also wrecked were a long line of taxi-cabs that had been parked along the side of the Square. The basement of a drapery store on the north side contained at that time a shelter used much by taxi-drivers and their families; hence the line of torn and empty chassis that faced the dawn next day. The blast had been strong enough to bend the back of one of these chassis round and up like the tail of a scorpion; but the explosion was most remarkable for the small human casualties —only sitting cases—and the fact that two wardens on a high roof over-looking the square saw the trouble descend yet lived to tell their tale (though they had the experience of being blown from one end of the roof to the other, of being nearly throttled by the chin-strap of a steel helmet).

Otherwise on that night blast damage was done to No. 10 Downing Street when a bomb fell in the gardens of Dover House. And the Theatre Royal at Drury Lane was set on fire—though not severely damaged. This together with innumerable other tragedies far and wide, and a long toll of death.

During the nights to follow, the Treasury was severely hit. The bomb was a small one, but it struck the mass of eighteenth-century brickwork behind the Whitehall façade, and reduced this to a rubble so entirely disintegrated, so flat that one could stand on the ground level and see straight over the debris. Two Treasury personnel were killed and buried under this huge weight of individually separated bricks: it was this incident that inspired an immediate decision to strengthen with steel girders all other government basement shelters.

Other bombs fell in Whitehall on the same night (17th October). The Horse Guards' Building—then headquarters of the Eastern Command—suffered damage to its frontage. A high explosive struck the footway a few yards from the Cenotaph, breaking gas and water mains but causing no fire or greater damage. The Colonial Office was struck, some of its parapet knocked down into the street. And on the same night there fell in the inner court of the National Gallery a bomb that failed to explode. This, in fact, remained where it was for several days. It was eventually dug out on the 23rd. The staff of a canteen which had been established nearby in the building continued to work, thinking the bomb unlikely to explode. To this canteen at their lunch-hour the bomb disposal squad retired. It was lucky they did so—as soon as they had gone off to lunch the bomb went off too.

Two further unexploded bombs of historic interest to wardens fell that week, one in Queen Anne's Gate and the other outside the Hyde Park Hotel. They were both confirmed as being small bombs exploded —the size of the craters merited this and of the bombs themselves there remained no trace. As time went on, road repairs were started: the various utility companies performed their long and intricate healing processes; the surfaces of the roads were relaid. Then months later, in mid-February of the next year, a lecture was delivered to A.R.P. personnel on the significance of the *kopfring*. They were shown examples of this metal attachment to the bomb that, when found separately, must always mean an unexploded bomb. It transpired that two of the audience at least had good memories—for both remembered finding such strange pieces of metal near to the two incidents mentioned above. Bomb Disposal officers were informed. The roads were opened up. Two very large unexploded bombs were found. They had lain dormant for four months.

Those mid-October nights continued with heavy action. There were severe incidents at, for instance, the complex by-way of Ham Yard off Archer Street—a place of small clubs and cafés by the Windmill Theatre; and at the Infants' Hospital in Vincent Square; and in Grosvenor Square; and in many, many other places. Westminster Abbey was hit by explosives and fire-bombs—but this damage will be surveyed in retrospect in a special section of this record devoted to the war scars of the great Abbey. Some bombs were still dropped by individual planes during daytime—but as the month wore on a gradual decrease could be noticed in the actual damage done, as indeed there was at last a real decrease in the scale of attacks.

However, just before noon on the 26th two unfortunate bombs fell in the West End. One hit the St. James's Residences in Brewer Street. It was a Saturday, and the market was crowded. The bomb struck into the red brick of the five-story dwellings—possibly less crowded than usual at that time of noon shopping. In this respect, it was better that the street itself was not struck. But however these cold comparisons may be, it proved a costly bomb with many casualties. Rescue workers were faced with a six hour job to deal with the extrication of the living—and to complete this they performed many dangerous and complicated manœuvres, involving among other things the picking through of party-walls and the jacking-up of three heavy floors.

Away from the crowded and tragic Soho street and over the rooftops to Mayfair and Curzon Street—there the second unlucky bomb fell on Curzon Street House, a modern brick block of steel-framed flats occupied then by the War Office. It so happened that a large number of workmen were engaged in painting the interior. These men had just broken off for lunch—for it was noon, and when the bomb fell many of them were in the lavatories washing. This fact that they were at the transition between work and leaving the premises provided again that problem so insoluble in the dust and hurry of those chaotic times— how many were there? How many wounded and killed should be found? . . . For lucklessly the bomb exploded near to the wash-place. This fact, and several contingent circumstances, made the case of this bomb a particularly involved one for rescue workers. Not maybe so practically difficult as others, but involved in itself as a scene, as an impact of chaos come suddenly in the noonlight. To begin with, there were many civilians on the streets. Though the bombed area was cordoned off, they thronged this cordon and in cases pressed forward in curiosity to break it. Morbid curiosity of this kind was not unusual; it is a familiar phenomenon, with its pathological excuses—but for rescue workers it was always an extreme annoyance. Coming from a building with a stretcher, coming from the inner scene of mutilation, coming thus at a pitch of urgent efficiency—it was nauseating to see the clean-clothed people peering forward with open mouths, horrified, horrifying, useless and obstructive. On this occasion it may be recorded that one such *voyeur* irritated a stretcher-bearer with his persistent intrusion to such an extent that the stretcher-bearer finally knocked him out there and then with his steel helmet. However . . . such severities were not the rule, and only the echo of disaster. For away from the crowded street and in the building the scene was ugly. To some it seemed that a curious gas had been used—for many of the wounded were carried out with faces and limbs a bright green colour. Paint. And inside there was more paint, red paint that in such circumstances resembled blood and complicated further the search among that debris of plaster, wet soot, and streaming water. Debris also of piles of treasury notes—for this was an Army pay office. Debris also in amongst which one badly cut and shocked doctor sat on a chair wrapped in a blanket, refusing to leave until he had attended to all the wounded.

It may be noted, too, that this bomb revealed an amazing engineering eccentricity. It struck the many-storied flats at the base, blowing off its stanchions an eight foot deep girder that supported the entire superstructure. This girder weighed as much as sixty tons—it had to bear above it a colossal weight. Yet—miraculously—the superstructure above, all the many hundreds of tons of brick, remained as if hanging in mid-air. Evidently it was held by other girders acting as cantilevers— but in those breath-taking moments the great hanging building provided a vertiginous and horrifying sight. It was shored up and much later that entire wing demolished.

Now for some nights there was raiding but very little damage. There were nights with no incidents whatsoever, and nights when there occurred only the explosion of an anti-aircraft shell. And then on November 3rd, London had its first raid-free night. At half-past five o'clock the sirens sounded their ominous and monotonous prelude— but an hour later the free liner-like note of the all-clear siren rang out! People waited. And nothing happened. The darkness remained free of further warnings—for the first time for fifty-seven consecutive nights.

The next day many Londoners thought that their dearly hoped wish had at last come true. There had been a gradual decline in the overall severity of raids; and this siren-free night represented for them the close of a week's diminuendo. It seemed that the pause, or perhaps the end, had come.

It hadn't. The next night saw the sharpest fall of bombs for some time —though it was not a large-scale raid. However, it gave the shape of things to come—for there was to be no real respite, November continuing as a month of frequent raids.

The nights of the 6th and 7th saw, amongst more serious developments, two incidents of a notable nature. One was the bomb that fell in Duncannon Street at the side of St. Martin's-in-the-Fields. Only superficial harm was done to the stone side of James Gibbs' beautiful church; but, as on many similar occasions when not much damage was done, there was loss of life. Here one solitary woman was killed. It so happened that she was carrying with her a cat—and it was by the collar on this cat's neck that she was identified. The cat itself lived, and a home was found for it in the Report Centre at the City Hall. It became the Report Centre's mascot. It was held to be the largest cat at least in London, it overflooded the Special Action Officer's letter-basket which became its choice of arm-chair during those long winter raids. That much is fact. But there is also a popular belief that the cat knew when the sirens were going to sound. It crept downstairs, they say, and installed itself in the letter basket some minutes *before* the air-raid messages came through. At least, if not to the cat, it is a tribute to German regularity.

The other peculiarity lay in the amount of bombs that fell on and in the neighbourhood of the Duck Island in St. James's Park. Half a dozen fell on or not far from the island on that night alone—and Duck Island was itself to receive at least six explosions of different calibres as its total reckoning of the war. The point, apart from the discomfiture of the pelicans and their smaller feathered friends, is that if one removed such a small area just a hundred yards or more to one side, then there would have been left to us no Downing Street, no No. 10, and perhaps no Winston Churchill.

On the afternoon of the 11th November, three bombs were dropped. Three bombs were not much for those days, but these three each took their toll of life and wounding—and one of them caused a major disaster. It was just after four o'clock, and a cold, drizzling day. Darkening then, and the people in the factories and offices around were getting ready to go home before the night set in. Some people had already left the printing works in Great Peter Street when the bomb fell that completely wrecked it—but there were many still on the premises. The plane—a lone raider—was seen, the imminent danger signal had been given, people hurried for shelter; and for this reason rescue parties had no idea how many workpeople had reached the shelter and how many were still on the stairs and in the passages. The debris was considerable and massed high, laced with heavy inextricable girders that ribbed the collapsed brick like the bones of some monstrous saurian. The heavy printing machinery lay weighing and hard inside. With the grey church behind, and in the falling darkness, and with a fire starting next door, there was presented to the arriving rescuers a sight ghastly in its tonal misery and tactically of the greatest difficulty. No one knew quite how to start, where to seek.

Then there was discovered a man on the top of the debris who had been precipitated with his office from the top floor; though injured, he was able to describe some probable places where the buried might have lain. Work was started. The drizzle grew to rain. Seven people were released suffering from injuries, with their clothes almost torn off. Ten were released uninjured. In one corner a broken roof hung over the operations of rescue, in danger of collapse; ropes were lashed to this, and guy lines taken to either side—where men, their hands numbed with cold, grasped them and held the roof steady. Those ropes were held throughout the night, and on until the next day; when hands relieved hands, they grasped over one another so that not a second's strain should be lost. Meanwhile the fire was developing in the other printing works next door, and spray from the firemen's hoses lashed over on to the debris. Rescue workers decided to approach the shelter underneath through the foundations of the church next door. These burrowings, slow and arduous, were completed—to find the shelter empty. The night raid was developing overhead, there was the sharp crack of anti-aircraft fire, the fall of bombs, the flash of livid light bathing this wreckage with sudden theatrical definition. It was found that in the wreckage lay a mass of blue-prints of the highest security—secret tank plans. Search was also made for these. A buried man was found, who while still buried gave instructions as to where other people might be found; while talking to the rescuers, his voice slowly petered away to silence. The building next door had flamed to that point just before the final gutting. In these conditions the night continued. Dawn came at last, but rescue operations were not finally concluded until four days later. Twenty-five bodies were recovered. Such was the toll of one bomb from one lonely afternoon raider. These small attacks by day were, in perspective, not trifling; at the time they seemed insignificant compared with the heavier night attacks—but often they caused fearful, if isolated, damage and death.

On November 14th the Luftwaffe struck its first heavy provincial blow—the great raid on Coventry that shocked the country and created that harsh word 'coventrated' (later to be translated into 'hamburgered'). This was the first diversion from London of any strength of German air squadrons, and thenceforward London was to receive roughly the same type of sporadic and heavy attention as the provincial cities—though with more intermediate alert periods. It received its first such attention on the night after the Coventry raid—on the night of the 15th November.

Curiously matching the date of the biggest raid of the previous month—15th October—this night saw for Westminster much destruction, including damage again to the National Gallery, also to houses of architectural interest in the St. James's area, also to the Wellington Barracks. In this latter case, canteen and recreation rooms were destroyed, but without heavy human casualty; the P.T. instructor sleeping on top of the building slid down on the wreckage and emerged unharmed into the street. The night was bright with fire—particularly a large fire at the north-west corner of Trafalgar Square, where a furniture company's premises was gutted. Severe incidents occurred in Pitts Head Mews in Mayfair, at the Carlton Hotel in the Haymarket, at Coburg Buildings in Greencoat Place and in many other places. A memorable feature of the night was the arrival in Shaftesbury Avenue of a gigantic unexploded bomb weighing one and a half tons. This monster was assessed by the Bomb Disposal squads and eventually removed two days later. The nature of its removal throws an odd light on the paradoxical feelings of the time. It was loaded on to a lorry, and driven away down Shaftesbury Avenue. Piccadilly Circus was cleared by the police. But shoppers and passers-by—it was three o'clock in the afternoon—pressed forward to watch the passage of this lorry as though it were part of a royal procession. Instead of taking cover, people lined the streets. A member of the squad on the lorry with the bomb recalls how driving through the lined streets he felt all the sensations of a curious type of dream, one aligned with the nightmare and familiar to many—the dream when one discovers oneself walking along the street without one's trousers on.

November ended without more heavy trouble, but with warnings on most nights and a few bombs. The tale henceforward is one of fairly constant alert and several sharp raids. December began uneventfully—but on the night of the 8th some three to four hundred bombers delivered a severe attack on London. Westminster itself did not suffer so heavily, though on such nights as this the feeling of activity elsewhere was felt by all, though indeed not much actual work devolved upon defence personnel. Severe damage, however, was done to the cloisters of the House of Commons—to offices, staircases and the basement crypt. The night also was memorable for the descent upon the Temple Gardens of a parachute mine which did great damage to the Middle Temple Library. And there was always—it must never be forgotten—amongst this historical destruction the breakage of smaller houses, and the loss of lives.

On the 11th December a surface shelter attached to Rogers House in Vincent Street was struck by an unlucky bomb—one of only three that fell that night. The other two caused much trouble also. One crashed into the great Hovis Flour Mill on the Embankment, demolishing equipment and making a large breach in the embankment wall, a matter of some concern for the River authorities. The other fell close to the east bridge of the Serpentine in Hyde Park. It proved to be the largest unexploded bomb that ever fell in Westminster—of a weight of 4,000 lb. It was also the most troublesome of all unexploded bombs, for as throughout the next days engineers dug the bomb continued to sink—a depressing foible brought about by subterranean water; infinitely depressing to those men sinking the shaft, for the monster took some ninety days to recover. But it was the third bomb at Rogers House that of these two had the most disastrous consequences. The casualty roll mounted to 65, the final death roll to 28.

The bomb fell at half-past ten. It exploded on one semi-surface shelter, and destroyed as well several adjacent flats. The next door shelter withstood the blast—and therein lies part of the tragedy. For it happened that many persons who might have been in bed, or who might have been in that next shelter, had been attracted to the shelter that was to be hit by the noise of raised voices. The argument was loud— something about who should sleep in the shelter—and people had crowded in to complain at such a noise disturbing their precious sleep. The bomb fell—with its tragic result. A lone unlucky bomb and an unlucky argument—the odds were thousands to one against such a coincidence. But the odds of bombing tended to be long. When the rescue parties arrived, they were faced by more casualties than usual; though with less difficulty in the actual rescue—for most casualties lay beneath only light debris. The scene was peculiar in one quality only—the first use of a loudspeaker van to direct operations from a central point. It proved in this instance immensely successful. Its voice was heard above all other noises: 'Twelve volunteers to shift concrete!' Or, when more planes came over: 'All lights out!' Rescue work continued to the sound of this voice, but it was not the last single voice that attended those twenty-eight dead. For this incident occasioned for the City of Westminster its only civic funeral. Some days afterwards a memorial service was held, and later twenty-one of the victims were laid to rest in Hanwell Cemetery.

Henceforth there was to be relative quiet—with the exception of sharp raids on the 29th December, the 11th January, the 8th March, and the two heaviest raids of all in April and May of 1941. But one incident four days before Christmas is worthy of mention. To this day it is a mystery. It was the lone explosive that fell on the night of the 21st December and struck the Southern Railway track near Ebury Bridge. It was the only German weapon that fell in London that night. It is still not known whether it was a plane, a parachute mine, or a bomb. Whatever it was, it was on fire. Observers talk of 'an orange glow in the sky, making a roaring noise, and moving rather slower than an aeroplane'. An officer of the A.R.P. Depot at Kingston House—far away in Knightsbridge—reports that it sounded as though they had dropped a *train* . . . and then the doors of the Kingston House First-Aid Post were blown in! Half-way down Sloane Street the roadway was already thick with glass. External damage was done to houses within a radius of a half a mile from the explosion. A four-foot length of railway line was found as far away as Chichester Street. Chair-bolts from the railway sleepers were found all over Pimlico the next day—as far as Chelsea Bridge. An entire iron signal gantry was blown off the line and dropped fair and square in the centre of Hugh Street nearby. The strength of this explosion can thus be imagined. But its cause remains a matter for speculation. Regional H.Q. considered it to be a 2,500 kilo bomb, one of only two dropped throughout the war. For a time it was the opinion of those on the spot that it must have been a plane—for parts of twisted metal were found all over the neighbourhood; but these were later diagnosed as the parts of products blasted from the windows of the Art Metal Company's premises near the track. Whatever it was, it went slowly enough for the Report Centre to receive five warning telephone calls *before the weapon reached the ground*.

Over the hard, frosty ground of that railscape and over the bleak skyline above the cut there was spread a vast and cold confusion. Houses were wrecked and blasted, the toll of casualties rose to the high level of 196. But only three of that large number were killed, an extremely small figure considering the wide area of damage and the high power of the blast (at the same time, it must be remembered that the explosion occurred on the railway track—and not in a populated street). Rescue operations were soon begun—it is recorded that to this incident, by virtue of its size and also of its isolated occurrence, there were sent no less than fifty-six vehicles of mixed rescue and relief services.

With such a large personnel in attendance, with the great number of casualties and in that heavily populated area—it can be well imagined that to a low-flying pilot the scene would have more closely resembled a disrupted ant-hill than most other incidents. Add to this weight of traffic and busying of people a further activity down in the railway yard itself, where some hundred Royal Engineers were called in to help railway engineers in the clearance of debris—for which special trucks were run up the line in order to get this vital link with the south operating as soon as possible.

However, no such low-flying pilot arrived—the night was blessedly free from further interference. It was bitterly cold, though, and the work was severe. A few isolated episodes in that wide bombscape of torn windows and glass and ruin may help to picture more closely the scene. An elderly woman, for instance, was found in her blasted-out house sitting over a stew-pot and mumbling to herself. She refused to leave the stew—muttering that she had taken a great deal of trouble in preparing it and none of those 'yellow Germans' nor anybody was going to stop her from finishing it. The stretcher party who found her were worried about her condition—she appeared shocked—and they tried to humour her into acquiescence. One of them asked for a taste of the stew. He put a spoon into the pot and found it full of plaster —and even bricks. A gramophone was playing from a house some doors away—through the empty glassless window, on this frosty night, sounding like a summer gramophone. It was playing a song called: 'All over the place.' Like the person who was playing this tune, the old woman was doing all she could to maintain 'face'. She was not so much angry as obstinate. Nothing would move her—by still stirring her stew she was putting the bomb in its place.

Over all that area there were scattered Christmas cards—for it was the evening of the 21st December. 'With love from Harry' and 'Best wishes from Elsie and Bill' were written in pathetic characters on these little pieces of paper in the street—while above them towered the strange new signal gantry and the space once occupied by an end house that had been completely blown away leaving no trace but its lowest foundations. It is one of the incredibilia of bombing that in the vault-shelter under the pavement in front of this vanished house there were found the next morning two people—unharmed but for the usual shock. It is also one of the constantly emerging surprises of human and in this case perhaps English nature that another woman found in a vault remained sitting on a chair, absolutely unperturbed, quite disinterested in the chaos surrounding her, and calmly stated that she was quite happy and intended to stay as she was until morning, when she would wash and then go to work. Meanwhile so near to her sitting on her chair, the grave work of tunnelling and difficult rescue was proceeding. Much of this proved that night successful. Especially notable was a case of the 'wheelbarrow' technique—an unusual method of extrication through a low tunnel when one rescue worker worms himself beneath the body of the wounded and allows himself then to be pulled out— more like a sledge than a wheelbarrow, a sledge to take the rough of the passage.

Christmas in London that year was quiet. The day after Boxing Day a light raid: but two nights later—on the 29th—there occurred the very heavy fire raid which burnt out so large an area of the City of London, and which extended over other parts of London in-cluding Westminster. The sirens sounded early—as usual on those long winter nights—and the raid developed in force. More fire-bombs than usual were dropped, though these were for a time well mixed with ex-plosives. The miracle occurred at some time past eleven. The all-clear sounded. The fires were then rising to a fury—it was a windy night and in the City of London the wind-spread of fire was on a gigantic scale. However, by some dispensation of the weather on German airfields the bombers never returned with the weight of explosives that would have aggravated so successfully an already disastrous situation. In Westminster the position was not grave—though there was trouble indeed, and of course a scarcity of fire-fighting appliances, for most had been drawn in force towards the City of London. Of particular incidents, the L.C.C. Ambulance Station in Regency Street was wrecked, and one of the war's largest craters opened outside the Egyptian Embassy—a vast hole measuring 42 feet across. Perhaps the greatest communal danger to the City was the fire at City Hall, in rooms just above the Report Centre itself. An oil bomb set fire to the Council Chamber on the first floor. The room became a mass of flames. Those on the spot ran the internal hoses straight to the fire—but there was no water, explosives outside had broken the vital mains. All that the fire-staff could do was to limit the spread of small fires in other rooms: meanwhile the main fire burnt on, one floor above the room controlling the whole of the City's defences. The official Fire Services arrived, but were faced with the same difficulty of obtaining water. Altogether this fire burnt for some four hours before it was thoroughly controlled—and throughout its quenching much water poured down the stairs into the basement. The low level of this basement was knee-deep in water—but fortunately the control room itself was raised a few steps higher. Interruption was caused to a main switchboard—though the important direct lines were not affected. These the control room staff kept operating throughout the period of the fire, when perhaps at any moment the blaze might have suddenly blossomed, as fires do, and brought the ceilings and floors above crashing down into the vital room beneath.

Relative quiet in the nights thereafter—but then the 11th January came, and with it one of Westminster's most serious multiple incidents, the destruction of a large fruit warehouse in Bow Street. It was the first high explosive of the evening, probably large, possibly armour-piercing—for it penetrated through five stories of the building and exploded then inside below the shelter. Possibly the bomb was fused with a slightly delayed action—but whatever form the explosion took, it collapsed the whole of the building down on to the broken shelter. The heavy floors caved inwards, weighing down on the general debris. A gas main was fractured, and it was gas from this that greatly hindered the rescue parties, for as time went on it formed pockets in the debris, pockets poisonous to the lungs and inflammable to the incendiaries that were shortly to fall. Twelve members of the company's notably efficient A.R.P. organization were on duty in the building, and some thirteen occupants of neighbouring flats were sheltering in the basement.

Rescue workers managed to get into the front of the building early—but no way was found to the shelter and the gas-pockets prevented further progress. Fortunately an official of the Council arrived who knew where the emergency exit to the shelter was exactly located, and how it worked—so that this was opened, revealing four people alive in a portion of the shelter that had remained intact. These four were rescued. But no one knew how the others were, or how to get quickly to the A.R.P. staff buried in different parts of the debris mound. The fire had started. In spite of the efforts of the Fire Service, it spread—and rescue work had in great substance to stop, though attempts were made from the basements of adjoining buildings. One further rescue was effected—the fortunate case of one of the A.R.P. staff who had descended, enclosed in a small steel shelter with the general debris. But he was the lucky one—to those working round the destroyed building it seemed that the buried were being burnt alive. A macabre sight—the wooden-blocked market street littered with bricks and vegetables and straw, the great iron and glass dome of Covent Garden reflecting on its remaining glass that bright firelight, the lion-coloured palladian columns of the Opera deeply shadowed, the spluttering roar of fire-engines, the snakes of dead-grey hose winding through the mud and water flooding the street, the stolid façade of Bow Street Police Station, the fire spreading all around. But most living of all in this street of nightmare were the unseen bodies entombed somewhere in the terrible breathing mound of debris. That was a powerless night for those standing, trying, failing. The odds were too great. But mercifully, when days later the last of twenty bodies were recovered, it was found that each one had died instantly with the bomb's explosion.

The night was otherwise memorable for an unexploded bomb in St. George's Hospital that necessitated a wholesale evacuation of patients. The bomb was of a difficult type containing a delayed action clockwork fuse—and de-fusing could not be attempted with any proper degree of safety. For this reason, too, the Bomb Disposal officer advised that underground trains running beneath should crawl at no more than five miles per hour. The patients themselves were successfully evacuated in a string of Green Line coaches. Otherwise incidents were scattered—and technically the bombing was notable for the heavier admixture of explosives with incendiaries; this might have been intended to discourage the newly formed army of firewatchers. For after the great

City fire on the 29th compulsory firewatching was finally instituted by the Fire Prevention Executive set up on the 3rd January.

Now for some eight weeks the City of Westminster recorded no incident. There were periods of alert, but no bombs fell. With the longest hours of the winter over, with the ominous twilight coming pleasurably later each week, and with the summer ahead—there was a real feeling of respite. Apart from severe sinkings of British tonnage at sea, and apart from the still-threatened German invasion, there was more hope abroad generally. Europe indeed looked black on the map— the Nazi territories looked overwhelming. But now in the deserts of North Africa the British were attacking most successfully, the Italians had yielded Benghazi. And the Greeks were beating Mussolini all along the line. There was cause for hope. Londoners were conscious of the battering of our provincial cities, there was no one who forgot the grave risks taken each minute of the year at sea. But now at last there were successes. And the Royal Air Force had started to hit back at Germany with a vengeance. In passing, it is interesting to observe that it was not until now that restaurant meals were restricted to only one main course. It was on March 4th that the first publicized commando raid was made on the Lofoten Islands, and it was on 8th March that London was again sharply attacked by a strong contingent of the Luftwaffe.

This was the night that the Café de Paris was bombed, when the Tate Gallery escaped with a broken bomb, when Buckingham Palace lost its North Lodge, when for some unaccountable reason some forty dud parachute flares were dropped in the Green Park, causing some concern as to the arrival of a new weapon. It was a dark night, without the bomber's moon at that time beloved by the Luftwaffe. Soon after half-past nine two 50 kilo high explosives crashed through the tall building above the Café de Paris restaurant in Coventry Street. One bomb exploded in the gallery just above the band, who with one exception were killed outright. The second broke on impact with the floor then crowded with dancers. A few minutes earlier the Garland's Hotel in Suffolk Street had been hit—so that the staff of the warden's post nearest to the Café were somewhat depleted. Those remaining were quickly on the spot, but confronted with a vast number of casualties they soon became immersed in First Aid work. This was to be expected —with injured and bleeding figures stumbling from the debris and calling for help. But it was the inevitable consequence that reconnaissance suffered. It led, in fact, to an incorrect message being sent to the Report Centre. The message requested assistance for one hundred *trapped* casualties. Trapping was a usual feature of Westminster incidents, concomitant with the general heaviness of the buildings. The Report Centre therefore took the call without question. They despatched two Heavy Rescue Parties for the extrication of the buried, one Mobile Aid Post to receive them, and two stretcher parties and two ambulances to remove the wounded as they were cleared. In point of fact, there were needed nothing but the Mobile Aid Post, ambulances and stretchers and plenty of them: for the debris was light and casualties were for the most part direct. Meanwhile, with the two ambulances already full, some wounded were removed in taxis—of which there were fortunately many in that district—and others were taken across to the hotel opposite, where a First Aid Post was set up. A little later the A.R.P. Controller arrived personally, assessed the true situation and sent back a call for the badly needed ambulances and stretchers.

Inside the restaurant, which was below ground-level, one powerful electric light had remained unharmed, throwing down a useful illumination for the work of rescue. Altogether there had been counted thirty-four fatal casualties. Over one hundred people were injured, a high proportion seriously. Many of these were women in evening dress and officers on leave. The blast of the bomb had destroyed much clothing—and eventually, since they were all visitors unregistered in any way, there was great difficulty in establishing identities. For weeks after, messages of inquiry were received from anxious relatives all over the country. The incident itself was closed some time before eleven o'clock, the work of rescue proceeding quickly after the initial delay.

Following this sharp and costly night in early March, there was again a respite for some weeks. Then came the heaviest raid yet, the eventful and terrible night of the 16th April, a landmark in time to the people of Westminster, and known to all Londoners as 'the Wednesday'.

But before recording this and the one other climactic night, it is perhaps the time to mention briefly those advances made since October in sheltering, post-raid and other facilities for the best and most even continuance of life under fire. Generally—for the more detailed picture will be given in its place later[1]—the whole organization of civil defence and the care of civilians had been readjusted since the days of surprise, speculation and indecision of the first six weeks or more. It is impossible to say exactly when this or that alteration was finally made, for such reorganization and rebuilding must of its nature be a slow business, and particularly so under the stress of bombardment—but in general most improvements were in being by the time of the great April raid. Much had been done as early as November, and then during

[1] Part II.

the months following—until some time in the first quarter of the new year the reorganization was complete.

Brick-blast walls now replaced the sandbags of the early days; bunks had been issued, so that people could achieve a night's rest in comparative comfort; electric lighting had been installed; lavatories with running water had been built. In the L.C.C. Rest Centres, where homeless people were taken for a period before proceeding to their new billets, great advances had been made in the methods of reception and of both accommodation and what was of primary importance—the provision of full-strength meals. These are only an indication of the many other improvements made during those few months, improvements ranging from the reinforcement of all surface shelters to the organization throughout the City of Fire Observer Posts on high buildings, from the training and re-training of hundreds of Civil Defence personnel to the provision of orderly ticket systems for the more populous shelters. Uncertainty of the enemy's next move, the difficulty of obtaining necessary materials, and the ordinary time-lapses of building and training were some of the reasons why this reorganization did not magically come into being during the first weeks: hard work, quick planning and a continuance of these under continual bombing were the means by which the reorganization was finally shaped. There were, of course, many things still to be done. War is always a period of development, the two opposing ingenuities constantly synthesize new conditions. There was yet to come, for instance, a properly organized civilian Fire Guard; and also the hard-pressed Fire Service itself had not organized emergency water supplies adequate to the real need. However, all in all, the picture was greatly changed from the harder, more chaotic first fifty-seven nights. Whatever was to come, those first nights were really the period of London's greatest stress.

The raid of the 16th April began in mid-evening. The night was fairly light, with a moon declining from its full phase of the previous Good Friday (this was the Wednesday after Easter). Berlin had been bombed on the night of the 9th, and although regular punishment was being inflicted on British provincial cities, there was some expectation that revenge would be sought on the capital itself—on a purely eye-for-an-eye passion declared vehemently over the German radio. The revenge came. As many as four hundred and fifty bombers were used that night over London. In Westminster 148 persons were killed, and 564 injured seriously. Towards two hundred high explosives struck the Westminster area, innumerable incendiaries, and eleven parachute mines. The high number of these mines tended perhaps to cause more trouble than any other single feature of the raid. It was the most congested of all nights at the Report Centre, where the staff had to deal with over three thousand messages, a figure that gives some idea of the widespread and complicated nature of this giant disruption of central London. The all-clear finally sounded at five minutes to five in the morning—a raiding period of eight hours. The incidence of such concentrated bombing cannot be chronicled in detail—street after street was hit and fired, house after house, as though several nights of early vintage had been contracted into the space of one. All services were strained to the utmost, and mutual assistance had to be sought from outside areas. That night saw no pause; when an ambulance or a rescue party returned to its depot, it went out again immediately. All utility services suffered damage. For the purpose of this record one can only select the most outstanding occurrences, and chiefly in this instance the devastation wrought by parachute mines.

An early and grave situation developed in the neighbourhood of Sutherland Terrace in Pimlico. Probably this is one of the largest single devastations caused in Westminster on any one night during the war, for on this one night Sutherland Terrace received the force of no less than three high explosives and two parachute mines. With the exception of three houses, the whole of the terrace of thirty odd houses was obliterated, and much damage was done around. The high explosives and one mine fell first. The second mine descended when rescue parties were already at work. The most accurate description of the scene as it faced rescue workers is a simple one: 'It was like Flanders'. Now this is seldom applicable to a blitz scene. In every case there is some configuration of building, some visible beginning and end to the catastrophic kernel. But here, in the night, in a place ringed with fires, the devastation seemed endless, a wide earthen space swelling with mounds and pitted with holes. In all the noise, in all the urgency of the moment, there was felt in the air that shroud of emptiness that hangs over a battlefield: when life has been blasted out of every square inch of ground, when the disintegration is complete. But, in fact, life was not altogether extinguished—though it was stunned. For several people were rescued. The tale of known deaths mounted finally to twenty, with the wounded at fifty-five.

When rescue and first-aid parties were already engaged on this field, engaged in what one heavy rescue man could only describe as 'digging, digging, digging', wardens away at a post in Glasgow Terrace saw through the flared and spitting skyscape the drifting pale glint of another parachute. It was coming in from the south of the river. The warden judged that it might land somewhere near Ebury Bridge. These mines are computed to travel at some forty miles per hour, but in the sky, during the moments of sighting that expand upon themselves to distort any ordinary experience of time, then the parachute seems to drift slowly, slowly, as light a thing as a seed—yet with an implacable oblique direction towards the roof. The warden telephoned the Report Centre —and while he was still on the line the mine struck—on Sutherland Terrace. The Report Centre heard the impact over the phone. Rescue workers on the site also heard it—and felt it more strongly than they had felt anything before in their lives. Over two thousand kilos of high explosive split over vehicles, men, wounded. Excavations made were filled in, men were killed and lorries blown up. A stretcher bearer remembers that 'it was just as though a huge orange flare had gone up under your feet. A hell of a bang. Then it was like a sandpapered ramrod down your throat, and your lungs puffing out like a pouter pigeon. Then dead, dead silence. Then, as though some time afterwards, a slow shower of bricks from everywhere'. This same man was buried up to his shoulders. His steel hat was blown right away. Fire broke out in the debris all around him. He would have been burnt, buried there with his head sticking from the hot ground, if others had not struggled over and dragged him out. He had his pipe in his mouth all the time. Later they put forty stitches in his scalp. . . . And only that morning, on such a fine April day, he remembered taking a turn in the park opposite the Kingston House Depot and strolling, at peace, by the new spring flowers.

Another man was blown a quarter of a mile—yet suffered only from shock, a broken heel and splinters in the face. He was thought to have been disintegrated entirely by the explosion—but turned up three days later on the lists of Hanwell Hospital.

This Sutherland Terrace affair was perhaps the most violent incident of that violent night. But major destruction was caused throughout the City. A factory in Grosvenor Road was badly fired, calling thirty fire-pumps and the attention of two fire-floats waiting on the river. Another parachute mine fell in Semley Place off Ebury Street. A great number of houses were again demolished, and a large Depository was set on fire and finally gutted. A powerful gas main was ablaze in the centre of this devastation, forcing an unusual divergence in the operation of services—in that the rescuers were separated by a wall of fire and thus had to work as at two independent incidents under two quite separate Incident Officers. It is memorable, and indicative of the greatest spirit of those times, that one warden on this job continued his work of reconnaissance and rescue in the knowledge that several streets away the house containing his wife and children had been bombed. He knew no details: nevertheless he continued with his work. He made no inquiry until after the first critical hour.

Another mine fell at Lillington Street, causing some forty deaths. It is interesting—and shows the chance of the time and place where these mines struck—to note that another at Dunraven Street caused only four casualties. Altogether eleven mines fell in the Westminster area that night—those at Jermyn Street and Shaftesbury Avenue causing otherwise the most casualties. This latter mine struck Newport Buildings, completely wrecking the bulk of these heavily populated, red brick dwellings. There were some forty-eight dead and as many as eighty-three casualties altogether. The Shaftesbury Theatre nearby was destroyed. Now, where these populous dwellings stood, there is cleared a wide space, flanked by the side of another tall block of flats, and on another side by what has become a common sight in bombed London—the revelation of a white-tiled wall never before seen. Such walls had faced inwards into those lightless wells that were once the glazed and grimed background to an iron machinery of service lifts and fire escapes, and so veiled from the streetman's eye. And here at Newport Dwellings, for instance, is revealed the back of the dark-brick Welsh Presbyterian church in Charing Cross Road—a back-wall of sudden bright white tiles, startling and strange in the open daylight.

Strange also was the behaviour of some elderly people whose homes familiar through the long declining years were wrested suddenly from them. Against the fiercest odds they tended to believe that their familiar things had not disappeared, that somehow life would right itself and the pack of cards magically be re-erected. Here, for instance, at Newport dwellings, an old woman was seen the next morning struggling over the rubble-mound with a garbage pail in her hand. She slipped on dislodged bricks, she circumvented painfully the jagged shafts of timber—and at last arrived at her destination, the exact spot where for years she had been required to empty the garbage from her flat. The dustbins were now hidden under a mass of brick, everywhere around for yards lay only muck and rubble and muddle—yet here still in this one familiar, instinctive spot the old woman tossed the garbage from her pail.

The final parachute mine to fall that night must be recorded, though it failed to explode. It fell on the northern end of Hungerford Bridge, and hung there on the superstructure of the bridge, endangering the embankment beneath, Charing Cross Railway Station and many important office buildings around (on the next day the War Office had to be evacuated). While it rested, precariously, a huge blunt pillar-box spidered around with its stays and its torn parachute, firemen of the London Fire Service fought a fire in a signal-box some yards away. The next day a naval officer arrived to inspect the mine, for mines were always attended to by the Admiralty. Clearing the bridge but for two assistants, he examined the huge canister himself, alone, in the cool light of day. He borrowed a piece of mirror from a shattered first-class carriage compartment. With this, he climbed underneath. He found there an extraordinary complication—the metal of the mine was actually welded on to the rail. It seemed that, although the electric current had been cut off, there was some heat in the rail which had caused such a hair-raising merging of weapon and prey. Nevertheless, despite the infinitely delicate nature of such work, the mine was removed successfully.

In the early morning of the 17th many incendiaries dropped on and around the Christ Church, Victoria. Prompt action from wardens and other helpers extinguished most of these, and incidentally saved the tower—but above the altar there was fire on the roof that could not be reached. The Fire Service was summoned, with a call for high ladders. Meanwhile under the burning roof, with heavy embers falling, wardens—including women—risked themselves to extricate the Bible and altar-pieces. But by chance an ember dropped into the organ— setting up instantly a great blaze. Then the main roof caught fire. The Fire Service arrived and set to work at a height with one of their 100-foot turntable ladders—those extendable steel ladders complete with hose that are commonly called 'water-towers'. For a time the sky above seemed quiet. Then the urgent spasmodic note of a Luftwaffe engine was heard, and a single plane circled above the church. It seemed to retreat, and then to come nosing back again. At last, as if scenting its chosen flower, it dived. A small high explosive came down to its horrid nest on the precarious water-tower reaching up towards it. One fireman was killed and five others received terrible injuries that resulted in death. The water-tower was wrecked, and so also a heavy pump alongside. Other people nearby were injured, but later recovered. The force of the explosion was so great that the wheel of one machine was sent flying against the wall of a bank across the street—incising on this façade the impression, still to be seen, of its tyre.

This was also the night when the Speaker's Residence in the Houses of Parliament was damaged by high explosive; the night of the wrecking of Stone's Chophouse, an historic eating place in Panton Street; and of the fire at Christie's Auction Rooms, the largest fire of a dozen in the neighbourhood, a state of affairs that kept fire crews on the job for a full twenty-four hours and the officer in charge on a turn of duty from eight o'clock on the evening of the 17th until three o'clock in the morning of the 19th. This fire situation, extraordinary in that a ring of fiercely burning buildings seemed suddenly to erupt at the very end of the night, when no aircraft could be heard above, was thought to have been started by a fall of incendiary leaves: these had for a time lain quiescent and then quietly fired, taking a grip on whole buildings, like Christie's and a large Building Society Office in the Strand, whose entire seven floors were seen suddenly blazing from top to bottom.

The Admiralty—including the Arch—was hit by several bombs—but the internal A.R.P. staff managed matters adequately. Among other buildings damaged were the Guildhouse in Belgrave Road, Charing Cross Station Hotel, St. Peter's Church in Eaton Square, the Little Theatre, the Royal Courts of Justice, the Farm Street Church, and Wellington Barracks. Damage was done to tunnels of the Underground railway, to the embankment wall, to mains far and wide. Barges were blazing on the Thames. Everywhere in the area roads were ripped up, houses demolished. The trench shelters in Leicester Square were hit, with casualties to shelterers. Among many of the freak situations created by bombs, there was an extraordinary incident in Denman Street. Here people were killed and wounded and a large crater blown in the narrow street. That, though grave, was usual—but it was not until some days later that repair men, digging in the crater, struck against a hard and unexpected substance. This proved to be steel—the roof of a saloon car that had been buried in the huge crater quite intact. Otherwise the night is remembered for its general ferocity; for helpless periods when the anti-aircraft stopped, and the sky was left to night fighters (an efficient protection, but illusive from the ground, where but for distant and spasmodic machine-gun fire one might have thought that the defences had really retired).

London was again raided heavily on the 19th April—the following Saturday. But the weight struck elsewhere than Westminster, and there were not more than half a dozen incidents in the area—all of a minor nature. However, it was one of the occasions when a bridge was hit—in this case both the new and temporary Waterloo bridges, each of which was struck by an explosive. A further bomb fell where many hundreds have fallen, into the Thames. The reason for this raid seems again to have been the German passion for revenge; for on the 17th April Berlin had received from the Royal Air Force its heaviest battering, until then, of the war. From then onwards there came a definite feeling to Londoner's minds that when Berlin was bombed, London would be raided soon afterwards.

In effect, London received no more attention until the night of May 10th, when the Luftwaffe delivered an attack of three hundred bombers. Strategically, this was the last of the big raids of the period known as the 1940–41 Blitz: though naturally such a cessation was not advertised, and for long afterwards London prepared itself for repeat raids. But it was the final fling before the Luftwaffe moved east to Russia. And tactically the night was outstanding for the great destruction wrought on the attacking force by shellfire and particularly by the guns of night-fighters. Thirty-three German bombers were shot down that night, a proportion of over 10 per cent of their number. It was a moonlit night, bright and clear. It was the final setting of what had until then been known as the 'bomber's moon'; henceforward the bomber chose the darker nights, for the night-fighter had proved its eyes.

Casualties for this May raid were rather less than for its companion of April, with 110 killed and 385 seriously injured (against 148 killed and 564 seriously injured in April). There were less parachute mines dropped, but more high explosives; and the fire situation developed more gravely than ever before in the City. It was a rather shorter raid in terms of time—lasting from eleven o'clock on the evening of the 10th May until nearly six o'clock the next morning. The Whitehall district itself was particularly damaged, though the raid was otherwise wide-spread. Again the field is so vast that it would be tedious here to re-iterate the course of the damage street by street. The whole area suffered and it was noticeable in the morning air that an invisible veil of plaster-dust hung its odour over the air of every street, bombed or not bombed, for Westminster was impregnated with it. Again one must isolate the most notable incidents, and let these imply the whole scene. In this respect the burning of the House of Commons and of the West-minster Abbey lantern and precincts were two landmarks of the night. But before examining these in the greater detail they deserve, account must be made of several other outstanding incidents. Early on, for instance, there was an unlucky hit on the trench shelters in Eaton Square, with eleven casualties. Two were killed; one of these being the Mayor, who had been at the time paying a voluntary round of visits to West-minster shelters.

Shortly after this, in Knightsbridge, a bomb crashed through the stairwell of the Alexandra Hotel and exploded in the centre of the building. The hotel was fully occupied, and the final toll of deaths rose to 24, with 16 others seriously wounded. The effect of the bomb's explosion brought down the lift shaft and demolished the main staircase—so that many people were isolated on the upper floors. This heavy inward fall of debris had a secondary effect, which was to collapse the foyer floor and smother those in the basement so that they were only rescued after several thick walls had been cut through. On the upper floors, rescue work was equally difficult. Again a cutting had to be made through walls—in this case through the walls of several bedrooms—to reach people isolated at the end of a blocked passage. A special feature of the incident was the loss of the hotel's registration books. Again rescuers were faced with the difficulty of speculating as to the number of victims, rather than knowing definitely from some list or known rota of habit how many people could be considered to be on the premises.

Three other hotels were struck in Vauxhall Bridge Road. There were 21 casualties, including 13 killed. Again there was a difficulty in ascertaining how many people were on the premises—but in this case for rather different reasons.

At Turner Buildings, a large block of flats on the L.C.C. estate at Millbank, a disastrous bomb completely demolished twenty-four flats. It passed right through the building, exploding below the foundations. It exploded, in fact, on the clay, on the ancient foundations of the old Millbank prison that had once stretched its grim radial corridors on this site. A large block of the brise-block Turner buildings was reduced to the ground and mostly to dust. Twenty-four persons were killed, and many others injured. However, one multiple rescue was effected early —twenty people trapped in surface shelters were brought out within one and a half hours. A feature of the incident was the obverse to experience at the Alexandra Hotel and other such incidents, for the census of persons on the premises had been kept absolutely correct, even to visitors, and this indeed helped rescue work most effectively. They knew where to dig, there was no time wasted in speculation and abortive attempts.

Two parachute mines fell—one on Mayfair Court and the other on the Palladium Theatre. In the case of Mayfair Court the four top floors were demolished for about a third of the length of the building—but considering the tremendous explosive force of those mines this provided again an outstanding example of the resistance to such severe stress of a modern steel-framed building. The Palladium mine fell over the stage and instead of exploding on impact penetrated the roof and caught its stays in the theatre flies. There it hung, precariously strung on the web of theatre ropes, a ton and a half of heavy steel and explosive, placing no one knew what strain on ropes that might at any moment have broken. Later it was removed unexploded by a naval squad.

At the back of Wardour Street, the quiet backwater of Carlisle House was rudely shattered, and the early eighteenth-century mansion completely destroyed. The Royal College of Surgeons building in Lincoln's Inn Fields was hit, and at this incident rescue workers had the strange task of rescuing parts of pickled bodies. Otherwise struck were St. Anne's in Soho, St. Michael's in Chester Square, the War Office in Whitehall, the London Museum (Lancaster House), Charing Cross Hospital, Curzon Street House, New Scotland Yard, St. James's Palace, King's College, and important lengths of the Underground railway tunnel between St. James's Park and Victoria stations. Victoria Station was hit several times, and there occurred at a neighbouring brewery an unfortunate killing of horses, when a high explosive made a direct hit on the stables; of twenty horses, twelve were killed, and the others led to safety.

Large fires scattered the area. With burst water-mains and slack hoses, the Fire Service were hard-pressed to organize adequately their emergency water supplies. The Children's Hospital in Vincent Square suffered fire damage, and one of the largest fires of the war in Westminster developed in the Palmolive Soap factory in Ranelagh Road, permeating the surrounding air with the smell of soap diluted in the hot water pouring out of the fire.

· But it was not until the morning that one of the last bombs to fall— and indeed one of the last bombs of the whole eight months' episode of Blitz—struck into the Central London Electricity Company's Bulk Electricity Supply station in St. Martin's Lane. The bomb exploded well within the building, which was of three stories. The upper stories and ground floor carried some 2,000 tons of machinery and large quantities of sulphuric acid. In great blocks of ten-ton transformers and rotary converters and the immense girders necessary to hold them, this vast weight was collapsed into the basement—where it sank down upon tanks filled with thousands of gallons of oil for the diesel engines. Five of the seven men on duty were dealing at that time with small incendiaries on the roof. They succeeded in battling their way down through the smoke and fire to safety: but the two others were killed. The collapse of machinery was not immediate but occurred within half an hour of the bomb's explosion and the start of a fierce and complicated fire. Thereafter the mass of oil and acid and debris boiled through the night in a dark and hidden inferno of twisted girders and huge iron automata—no flame was seen, but the heavy lamp-black smoke of burning oil flooded out and up to form a pall over the sky that darkened Westminster's dawn. The soot was, in fact, so black that later, when the basement was surveyed, torchlight was useless—for there was no surface anywhere which would reflect light: only dark, absorbing black. For a time water was not available, but finally the Fire Service were in action with artificial foam directed to smother the fire beneath. Water merely spreads an oil fire; this thick, creamish foam blankets it, excluding the breath of oxygen by which the flames live. In time a great pile of foam tins blocked the street; from the black-gushing wreckage there sprouted huge dead girders and the awful twisted mass of lifeless cable; overhead the sky was devilled with flying rags of black burnt paper drifting from a burning dump south of the river; such was the end of a wreck that took as long as seven months to clear finally of its debris, the remains of a station that had supplied an electricity load equivalent to that used by a town of 60,000 inhabitants.

But the two most celebrated fires had already started some hours before. These were the occasions of the Abbey Lantern, with the Abbey precincts and Westminster School; and of the burning of the House of Commons. Both these experiences should be surveyed in some detail—and with reference to their total wounds of war. First, Westminster Abbey.

Until May 10th the Abbey was comparatively little damaged. Glass had been blown out on several occasions—the Great West window, windows of the Jerusalem chapel, the Chaucer window in the south transept and the Henry VII chapel windows suffering particularly. The blast in the Henry VII chapel also brought down two bath-stone pendants from the ceiling—one of the finest examples of a fan-vaulted stone tracery roof in Europe. Stone screens round the chapel were moved, but no irreparable damage was done.

Dean's Yard and other of the precincts were not so fortunate; early on a high explosive bomb had penetrated the Choir School at first-floor level, doing considerable damage; and oil bombs had thrown their contents over Dean's Yard and the Little Cloisters, though resultant fire damage was not heavy. As time went on further blast was felt in Dean's Yard and then on October 19th, 1940, a high explosive came down through the roof of the Busby Library in Westminster School—this time causing heavy wreckage, with again blast damage to the adjacent cloisters. On this night an incendiary fell through the roof of the Jerusalem Chamber—the tapestried conference-room by the chapter office: but this was quickly put out. On 8th March upwards of

fifteen small incendiaries were scattered over the Abbey and its precincts—up in the South-West Tower, on the precarious roofs, and again
around Dean's Yard. All these fires were extinguished without spreading by the Abbey's internal fire organization.

From this point of view of fire protection the Abbey presented many
difficulties. A gothic building of such size is of its nature complex.
Though its roofs and towers are on the whole accessible, they are high,
extensive, involved. Around the internal main body of the Abbey, and
at a height of sixty feet, runs that wide corridor called the Treforium.
Hoses fed by internal hydrants are mounted here, and attack could thus
be made from the Treforium on to the roofs outside. Ancient stone
spiral staircases lead up to this height within the walls—and from
thence on to the roofs other difficult stairways must be negotiated,
simple in the quiet of day, but physically some strain in the urgent
running moments of the night. The stairs up the colossal towers were
similarly stringent; on one night a firewatcher had to run up the tower
stairs three times to locate the glow of an elusive incendiary—the light
could only be seen and marked from the ground—and coming down
for the third time his legs literally failed, they froze suddenly stiff in a
kind of temporary muscular paralysis.

But returning to the main roofs—observer posts were positioned at
tactical points, and here, at nearly one hundred feet above ground-level,
the Abbey firewatchers spent their blitz-nights. Areas of these roofs are
flat and safe and solid, like the secure decks of some enormous stone
ship. The pinnacles, the spires, the buttresses that appear from the
ground reasonably diminutive grow huge in this strange and isolated
land above. It is as though one stood in a new city of white and black
stone, each pinnacle above and below glinting like the spire of a separate
church, with the flying buttresses presenting an architecture quite new
and of no formal meaning. The ground below is forgotten, only this
queer, beautiful but unintelligible island exists. Such an edifice flickering in the reddish reflection of London's fires must have been a memorable sight—with around the black sea of the streets dotted here and
there with fires, like pools of red phosphorus.

But the isolation was not, of course, complete. All the accoutrement
of firewatching lay to hand. Hoses, sand, shovels, and telephone communication with the ground floor and the Abbey control-room quartered in the eleventh-century Pyx Chapel. And if there was wounding
above, or some isolating spread of fire, then there was offered a means
of swift escape alternative to the dizzying slow spiral staircase; for at
one corner of the Treforium a wooden cradle had been erected, and

block and tackle fixed, so that the wounded or the escaping could be lowered through the sixty feet to the Abbey floor.

But however much these Abbey firefighters did to save their tall island in the first months, the situation on the night of May 10th proved too much for them. In the first place, the mains had been broken by high explosive, and although the Treforium hoses were run into position, those incendiaries that had ignited the Lantern could not be controlled: the hoses were dry and useless. The fire took a hold, and soon the whole Lantern roof was burning furiously. Meanwhile buildings in the precincts and in Westminster School were ablaze, and there the regular Fire Service was in attendance. A call was put out for pumps and ladders to come to the aid of the Abbey itself. Several fires—in the South-West Tower, and on the Nave and Treforium roofs—had already been extinguished by the Abbey fire-guard. The Library roof had been set alight earlier, and water storage tanks had been exhausted in attempts to extinguish it; these had been almost successful—when the supply of water ran out. So that with such an involved fire situation and with no water the Abbey fire-party could do little until the arrival of the Fire Service with ladders and emergency water supplies. The Lantern roof was ablaze at a height of 130 feet, and embers were dropping on to the Abbey floor. The only thing that could be done was done—all chairs and other furniture were dragged from beneath the danger area; this may sound simple, but the number of chairs in the great Abbey even in that one place was considerable, and whoever went beneath the Lantern risked death from falling debris and from streams of boiling lead that fell down echoing through the 130-foot drop. Finally, before the Fire Service arrived, the Lantern roof collapsed. In the light of day, this loss was not great—for the Lantern had already been burnt out in 1802 and the replica was not of outstanding value. However, there was always the danger of fire-spread; but this was finally controlled by the arrival of the Fire Service emergency water. All this time, too, there was severe high explosive bombing well within earshot—for such is the construction of the Abbey, with its high windows and stone auditorium, that the noise of any bomb falling within a mile's distance resounded as though it were, in fact, dangerously near.

In the cloisters there was more trouble. Severe damage was done to this little square of the Canons' houses, a quiet place with a small court and a fountain. The next morning the courtyard of shaded grass was open to the light, the little houses were in ruins, and across the garden the Westminster Upper School revealed its roofless walls. It was an unhappy sight, for until then the Abbey had so largely escaped. Now there were deep scars. The Upper School, formerly a monk's dormitory in the sixteenth century, was empty and open to the skies; the names carved in stone by scholars through the years were blackened and seared. Across the garden another house, with its remaining Italianate arches, stood strangely dramatic, like a red-brick folly from some eighteenth-century park. Otherwise—the library roof was wrecked, the Lantern was gone, and the floor a mess of rubble. Yet with all this, the Abbey had been saved. Watchers on the roof of City Hall had looked westward that night and, seeing the great towers and spires outlined in the firelight, had thought it the end of the historic Abbey of Westminster. But the Abbey was to survive the war. With 60,000 sandbags sacking its remaining monuments (many of which had been removed for the duration), with emergency water-pipes laid and iron scaffolding and ladders erected round its high walls against a recurrence of so dangerous a fire situation, with new tanks of water on its green and a constantly exercised fire staff—the Abbey remained untouched for the rest of the war.

The group of parliamentary buildings known as the Palace of Westminster had a somewhat similar war experience to that of the Abbey, in that the main damage was done on this same night of May 10th; but the bombing up to that point had been rather more severe and certain further damage was to be sustained in the raids to come in 1944.

The Palace contains five miles or more of corridors and about one thousand separate rooms. The geographical problems facing an A.R.P. staff are patently immense. Added to this, the Palace is a place jealous of its privileges, and only internal A.R.P. organizations were permitted to work in its precincts—unless it was found that matters had got beyond all possible local control. And again added to this, the various sections of the Palace—that, for instance, occupied by members of the Commons as opposed to the territories of the Lords—such sections were in turn jealous of various domestic privileges, so that further complications were added within to the organization of a comprehensive A.R.P. body. Precautionary measures were taken against any intrusion upon each sacrosanct threshold. And as it affected outside bodies, for example, there had to be obtained special permission before even a fire-engine was allowed to enter the gates. Such orders were real enough in terms of security, and were not in this way different from most other independent bodies along Whitehall; only more so. It must be added, however, that if the saving of life was in question, all obstruction was naturally waived; but up to this point a situation of most involved diplomacies obtained, not in practice an unsolved encumbrance, but none the less a matter of extra work and complication.

As time went on some seven to eight hundred persons formed the A.R.P. staff, which was recruited from the Palace's officials and artisans —secretaries, doorkeepers, electricians, French polishers and others. A rescue service was formed from builders in regular employ. The organization—as with many A.R.P. services—was not geared to its greatest efficiency at the beginning of the Blitz; the experience of May 10th provided the final stimulus, and the above strength of personnel was achieved in the late spring of 1941.

Parliament sat in London throughout the 1940–41 Blitz, although its residence was moved from the Palace to Church House nearby. Though the new council chamber was not located underground, at least greater protection was obtained, for in the Palace only one unprotected roof was interposed between the bomb and the member. A move was made to Church House on the 7th November, less officially than as a test to see how Parliament would function there. Then, on the 20th, Parliament was prorogued at the Palace and the King reopened his assembly at Church House on the 21st November, 1940. This was the first time that Parliament had been opened away from the Palace for many decades. The tendency thereafter was to sit in the Palace when possible; but on some occasions in the early spring Church House was again used. They had, for instance, moved back into the Palace just before the great raid of May 10th. They returned in June, the Commons taking over the Lord's Council Chamber, and the Lords sitting in the King's Robing Room. Later the two bodies returned to Church House at the time of the flying-bombs, and there they remained until the 3rd August of that year.

Before returning to the narrative of the bombing itself, the parliamentary Home Guard company must be mentioned. This was again the result of a wish for independence, of the ship-like quality of a Palace moored on the Thames and separate in all spirit from the land. Before the Palace was built, the Duke of Wellington had directed that this site by the river should be chosen—for military reasons—as against an alternative proposed for Regent's Park. The water barrier might have served well in those days, or at any time of severe civil disturbance; but in days of aerial bombardment it acted merely as an excellent guide to any pilot who had either the time or the desire to aim his bombs with any precision. However, in the rigorous course of Home Guard exercises, the Thames parapets were in fact defended—and during the most comprehensive of London's military exercises, the exercise called

'Genesis', a party of soldiers did approach by river and scaled the wall. These exercises were often regarded by outsiders as a sort of toy soldier game; but the effort was great, the need great, the terms rigorous—so much, in fact, that one member dropped dead during a most energetic night exercise.

The first bomb to hit the Palace was an oil bomb that failed to ignite. It broke through into some offices, it made a mess. No more. Then, on 27th September there exploded in the roadway the bomb that blasted many windows and bent Sir Richard Cœur de Lion's sword. There were near misses in the river, but on the 8th December a high explosive fell a few yards from Westminster Hall in Cloister Court. This caused considerable wreckage, and destroyed a number of important documents. One side of the gothic court was strewn over the paving; later, long after the debris had been cleared, among the rosebay and other weeds that so quickly took root in London's ruins, there grew in this case a few green and feathery ferns—oddly apposite to Pugin's gothic Victorian interior.

On the 17th April an explosive fell on the Speaker's House, damaging the structure and bringing down from the roof a water tank that flooded its supply through the house. On the 19th an unexploded bomb of 250 kilos also came to earth in the same house, but this time no damage was done and the bomb removed safely.

Then—the night of the 10th May. Incendiaries fell early. Again, as at the Abbey, the roof-land of this immense building is a complicated and diverse affair. A succession of small flat spaces, many oblique roofs, many courtyards dropping sheerly their squares between the interlaced buildings. Crevices, ledges, little variegated knobs of stone abound everywhere—it is an ornate edifice, complicated even at such a height with such decorative minutiæ as small green crowns and gilding on some of the stone and iron designs. Each one of these myriad ornaments became a possible fire-trap. And even if no fire resulted, then the light generated by a bomb was itself dangerous, for it would have thrown a brilliant lantern across the whole building. However, those waiting in the watcher-posts on the roof were able to contain any incendiaries that fell. But it was not so round the Victoria Tower, for this was meshed with scaffolding used by cleaners of the limestone. There had previously been much concern as to the danger invited by this scaffolding and its planks. Any incendiaries caught up there would burn untouched and throw their perilous light over the immediate area. Exactly this occurred on the night of the 10th. And it became the occasion of one of the most spectacular single actions recorded in the open in the Blitz. A police-sergeant, seeing the dangerous light, climbed up the outside scaffolding to the incredible height of three hundred and fifty feet. He carried a heavy sandbag to extinguish the bomb, his almost vertical path was made up of only the narrow and steeply-set ladders zigzagging skywards among thin steel scaffolding poles. He achieved this prodigious labour, and extinguished the bomb.

The first high explosive struck an octagonal tower above one of the westerly courtyards, just above the level of the royal gallery. Only three minutes earlier two auxiliary police had been stationed there. Theirs was the most unlucky chance—they were both killed. The bomb sliced off the turret and an avalanche of debris was hurled down into the courtyard. This debris became immediately a source of trouble; for in the intricate network of corridors and courtyards, one such blockage meant deviation and loss of time in the dark and urgent moments running through so vast and complex a geography. The next bomb to fall also caused a block. It fell on a bridge in the centre of the building, precipitating much debris into the free passage beneath. Meanwhile an unexploded bomb had crashed through the roof over the A.R.P. control-room, and penetrated to the basement beneath the passage-way outside. This control-room, the hub of the internal A.R.P. system, was positioned in the eastern part of the building; at the opposite end, in fact, to the House of Commons. To visualize the main aspect of a map of this building, and of the affairs that night, it might be easiest to imagine as the inner bulk a square-moulded hour-glass; the top section is the westerly House of Lords, with the Victoria tower on one topmost corner and the control-room pocketed at the other topmost corner. The bottom segment of the hour-glass is the House of Commons and all easterly buildings; in the middle are connecting rooms, and already some debris from the bridge. Around the whole runs a maze of corridors and excrescent buildings: but the hour-glass comprises the inner bulk.

Now, at this time, the A.R.P. personnel were rather concentrated on the House of Lords end, the westerly end. There had been the killing of the two policemen. There were incendiaries. There was the debris at the narrowing of the hour-glass. There was now the unexploded bomb beneath the control-room. And meanwhile, at the other end of the building, bombs had caught the House of Commons, starting a fire. Outside assistance had been called for: but owing to the intricacy of the building's layout it was difficult to explain (over the connecting telephone, which still held) many of the complications of the building to those newly arrived at the other end. Meanwhile it was decided to evacuate the control and move it nearer to the other end of the building. Only one man remained, and one woman. This was the doctor and his attendant nurse. He refused to leave a wounded man who needed an immediate operation. There was a slender chance that quick action might save this man's life. The doctor operated there and then with the unexploded bomb beneath the floor upon which he worked. But the man died, three-quarters of an hour later. Through the dark passages the control staff moved east. Meanwhile incendiaries had fallen all over the eastern end, starting small fires, and one particularly in the roof of Westminster Hall. The Fire Service concentrated most of their pumps here, finally, in fact, saving the historic building, though this meant abandoning temporarily the House of Commons.

Altogether, the situation grew too complicated for the resources and and the personnel available. When the House of Commons took fire, it burnt furiously, with all the draught of a grate, for beneath the floor lay the labyrinthine channels of a great heating system that fed the air in the House through grills set in the floor. It developed into a blaze needing forty fire-pumps and two days' work. The fire itself had a buckling effect on the roof trusses, and stonework of the outer walls was expanded in the great heat. Finally, the roof collapsed; and in the morning there was nothing left of the famous House but a charred, black, smouldering, steaming ruin. The Bar no longer stood to check intruders. The Speaker's chair was lost. The green-padded leathern lines of seats were charred and drenched. The ingenious, ingenuous, most typical gothic innovations of the old period had gone for ever; and with them the Chamber, its Press Gallery, its Strangers' and Ladies' galleries.

The all-clear sounded at ten minutes to six o'clock. Dawn filtered over a shattered London indeed, and a most disrupted Westminster. The black pall from the supply station fire stretched darkly over the sky, the air was rich with the smell of burning wood and poisonous with the fine grit of exploded buildings. Many landmarks had gone, many historic buildings would grace the City no longer. The process of clearing up began, and continued through the following days. Meanwhile, the A.R.P. organizations braced themselves for a further assault. These raids were increasing in weight. They seemed to occur every month—sometimes in pairs (as in April). In the Westminster records there had been up till now recorded 1,620 incidents. They waited for number 1,621. But the rest of May was quiet, with no bombs dropped; and the first part of June passed without the heavy raid expected. Then, at four o'clock in the morning of the 22nd of June, there occurred what might enter the records at least as Incident 1,620a. Germany invaded Russia.

Thereafter began the period known as the 'Lull'. The Luftwaffe moved its heavier bombing forces to the Prussian and Polish airfields. The London Blitz was over. No raid in any strength was to occur until January 1944, two and a half years later. But, of course, nobody knew that. Serious possibilities were still envisaged. Rumours went round of 'a third of the Luftwaffe still in France'. And of 'new, giant planes specially built for England'. At that time German resources seemed inexhaustible. And London foresaw no respite—though as time went on, and the Luftwaffe remained away, an ambivalent feeling of security again crept over the capital. Yet, in the general theatre of war, the hopes of March had been reversed. The Germans had taken the amazing Greeks in the rear; Greece and Crete had been captured, with heavy British losses. In the North African desert, our earlier successes were being reversed, and the Germans had forced us back to Sollum. Alexandria was being raided. All central and south-eastern Europe was becoming part of the Axis bloc. Turkey had signed an agreement of friendship with Germany. Atlantic sinkings were considerable. Certainly the Bismarck had been sent to the bottom; certainly America seemed to be stiffening her attitude towards Germany. But things looked black—and never more than on the map.

To the man in the street Germany's invasion of Russia did not immediately mean much. There was the thought that certain economic help was lost to the Axis, that much of the German army would be involved in the drive east. But the drive proceeded quickly. This speed, and ignorance of the true extent of Germany's diversion of forces, left little room for real confidence that an invasion of this country was excluded. It was, then, in no spirit of immediate relief that England and London faced the quiet months to come.

Over all the period of the Blitz the people of Westminster and its visitors suffered casualties, as far as can be ascertained, of 786 persons killed, 1,338 persons seriously injured, and 624 recorded slight casualties, of which there were, of course, many more unrecorded. These deaths and woundings were the result of a bombardment by 1,047 high explosive bombs of mixed designation, 180 unexploded bombs, 55 heavy oil canister fire-bombs, 11 parachute mines, 4 unexploded parachute mines, and small incendiaries the number of which cannot be counted but ran into many thousands. On these figures, there was thus represented an average of 0.71 fatal and of 1.21 serious casualties for each exploded bomb. These averages seem surprisingly small. Such a clinical assessment must be balanced against the imagination of those who endured the bombardment; in terms of human perception, at the height of the raids and in the sour and empty aftermath, the casualties and the possibility of becoming a casualty seemed far greater than the objective figure that can now be written on paper. It is an old argument. It must be left to individual judgment as to what embodies the final truth—the material happening isolated from the moment's heat; or the fact, however distorted from material measure, as felt subjectively by those who lived the experience.

The narrative of those months has now been told in chronological order of those events that seemed to be of the greatest importance. Now the picture must be completed by some illustration of the small happenings that went to make up the greater pattern. To recapture the feeling of the extraordinary, the sudden, the chaotic, the comic, the tragic, and even the dulling quality of those times, it is best to employ no order but merely to list, heterogeneously, paragraph by paragraph, some of these events that formed the night kaleidoscope.

One Sunday morning, for instance, a bomb exploded in a public house in Mayfair. The Sunday dinner was on, the maid was walking upstairs, the licensee was reading his paper and his wife was taking a bath on the top floor. The bomb shattered the building, killed the licensee, sent the maid sliding down the falling banisters bruised but unhurt—and precipitated the bath with the lady still in it into the centre of the road. She was shocked, bruised, but otherwise—in her bath in the middle of the disrupted Sunday morning street—unhurt. The dinner still simmered on the stove.

When people were buried under tons of heavy debris, they sometimes survived by the one chance in a thousand. There was one case of the man buried for a night with his family around him killed—and who survived because a percolation of water from a broken pipe dripped across his face. One of the longest burials of the war occurred at a Knightsbridge incident. A girl lay buried for forty-eight hours. She was protected from the crushing weight above her by a propped up slab of concrete. She lay only semi-conscious throughout, and said afterwards that her main discomfort was caused by dust choking the little air she could breathe. Her first request—as was often the case—was for a cup of tea and a cigarette. Again, at Dover Street a girl was buried for twenty-four hours under a table. The fact that the debris was burning is thought to have kept her alive, for the fire was not too near yet kept the debris warm, and at the same time provided a draught of ventilation. She was conscious and apparently well when finally extricated, and commented to her rescuer that this was her lucky day. She had been buried on a Saturday; but the rescue man replied, 'Better the day, better the deed.' She realized then suddenly that it was Sunday, that she had been buried for a whole day and night—and she passed clean out.

Horses were the special concern of the men that looked after them, and of the National A.R.P. Animals Committee. Men leading horses from a fired building used to throw a coat over the leading horse's eyes and muzzle; the horse was then more easy to control, and others occupying the same stable were apt to follow this leader. One stable employed a goat as a leader—for horses are supposed to follow with some alacrity this surprising beast. One horse that had been bombed never forgot the experience; whenever afterwards it passed a bombed building it shied; so chronic was this affliction that the horse had to be superannuated to the country.

Stories of rescue work abound. One heavy rescue man, faced with a collapsed building and a woman hanging from a hole in the ceiling by her hair, was forced to cut the hair to free her—and received a slap in the face for his trouble. In another case, a man was trapped and rescue work, in view of certain special circumstances, proceeded very slowly indeed. The casualty became very weary of this protracted situation and finally asked the rescue people above him to get a move on or else he would come up himself and give a hand!

In the darkness and urgency of those broken streets the night was full of misunderstanding and muddle, despite the best-laid plans and manœuvre. Once a warden conducting reconnaissance work asked a man at the door of a badly blasted house if there was anyone due to be in the building when the bomb fell. He replied: 'Only the boiler man.' The warden found out from him where the boiler-room was and went in to make his search. The building was flooded at the time, and the warden was faced with a long and dark time in a basement waist-deep with water. He persevered diligently—but found no floating corpse. At last he returned to the man at the door and tried to elucidate further upon the matter. Asking then another question about the boiler man, the reply received was: 'Oh, *I'm* the boiler man.'

But the scene was often—naturally—more muddled to the bombed than their rescuers. One rescue service worker was searching a building for stray casualties, when he heard the voice of a woman calling faintly for help. The sound came from an upstairs room. He went up, and traced the voice to a room from which the door had been blown off. It had fallen across the bed and was resting on the woman. She could have easily pushed it aside and freed herself. Instead she had lain there for some time under the impression that the whole house had collapsed on her and that one move might have occasioned a further avalanche and the loss of her life.

Sometimes the horribly wounded had no idea of their real predicament. One man with his eyes blown out thought himself only temporarily dazed. The force of the injury had numbed him, he thought he was only 'seeing black' for a few moments. It was with the greatest difficulty that wardens persuaded him to remain where he was on a stretcher. Otherwise he would have gone immediately to his wife, who was somewhere in the very near vicinity, and would have walked into her room—to soothe her nerves during that particularly fierce night.

Another man, with all the fingers blown off one hand, was found scratching his head, with the hand an invisible finger's-length from his scalp. In such a numbed condition the instinctive measurement of years was still guiding his movement.

Wardens and other observers were always on the alert for poison gas. There was no moment during the war—particularly perhaps in this first phase—when a poison gas attack might not have developed. Early in September, for instance, Fire Service reinforcements were seen driving through Westminster eastwards to the City mounted on their machines and wearing gas-masks. The gas warning had gone out. A tell-tale stench of peardrops was on the air. But finally the trouble turned out to be no more than a warehouse containing real peardrops on fire! Other false reports reached the Westminster Control. One case was due to smouldering cardboard sending out a particularly nauseous and suspect fume. In another, the reason was the destruction of a refrigerator, from which was released a filling of ammonia that evaporated with a lachrymatory effect.

One of the humbler yet most simply pathetic stories of the whole Blitz was the case of a missing body. There had been an explosive incident, with deaths. The dead had been laid out in a nearby house commandeered as a temporary mortuary. The bodies had been counted and otherwise checked. So that it was with some surprise that later on in the night those in charge found one of the bodies to be missing. They made a recount, searched in every reasonable way, considered every possibility, and finally called in the police—for it was just possibly a case of body-snatching. Finally, long after, the mystery was solved. A friend of one of the dead had looked into the room and had noticed 'old Alf' lying there on the bare boards in that grim and pathetic company. It had been too much for him. 'Old Alf' should not be allowed to spend the night in so desolate a place, so forgotten, so alone among the other dead. Alf's friend had simply picked him up and carried him off to his own home. . . .

Small matters often troubled people more than the greatest disaster to their homes. In one blasted house a man was rescued from under a billiards table. He seemed not over-worried about the house, but very concerned about a gas meter. 'Every time I touch it,' he said, 'its hands go round and it hisses at me.'

On another night, two clerks of works in the rescue service were investigating two unexploded bombs. They saw and confirmed one—in fact at Punch's Club in Waverton Street—and then before proceeding to the second decided to phone the control from a call-box in the club. The line was engaged. They went on to the second bomb. During this second investigation they heard the first bomb explode. They returned, and while going through the wreckage found the telephone kiosk which they had used some little time before. One of them had the happy thought of pressing Button B. He got his twopence back.

A man strolled out of his house in Pimlico to see what the night was like. It was busy. And the business at that particular moment was largely provided by a parachute mine that chose to strike a street not far away. The man reported feeling 'a queer sensation'. He was not blown over. He remembered no violent buffeting or blasting. But he suddenly felt the pavement through his feet. He looked down. His slippers had disappeared.

An esoteric of naval gunnery surprising to laymen was revealed when a naval officer arrived one morning at a brewery in Westminster. The officer had been firing on the previous night, he said, from Greenwich; and he had lost one of his shells. He had reason to be sure from his calculations that the shell would be found in the brewery. This was in the Victoria district. Directors of the brewery disclaimed all knowledge of any shell arriving on the previous night. Such a visitor would have been assuredly noticed. Nevertheless the officer was convinced. A thorough search revealed nothing. However, extending the field of possibility a few yards from the brewery walls and into a nearby build-ing, there sure enough, they came upon the shell—a traveller of the great trajectory from Greenwich to Victoria.

One evening a call came to the Berkeley Square depot for a heavy rescue party. Soon the lorry was on its way, loaded with its crew, swinging out into Bruton Street. A high explosive fell, hitting the side of the houses, blowing up the lorry and injuring all its occupants. One of these wounded men—with both of his legs so severely hurt that a few days afterwards he died—first did as much as he could for the other wounded men, and then crawled some fifty yards back to the depot, through all the debris and glass and mess that circumscribed the explosion, for assistance. This most heroic action seems to stand out among the records; perhaps the more for the knowledge, gained of course afterwards, that the call for that vehicle had never been really necessary, it was the result of the sometimes inevitable, distorted but so human muddle of the moment.

The great pattern was evolved against a sharply monotonous background, always with varied surprises, deadening to the tired senses, vitalizing with sudden violences, a hotch-potch time of paradox, strain, pain, hard work, fidelity and often of laughter. A girder is blown from Charing Cross to Parliament Square, a shopful of Covent Garden grapes are saturated with powdered glass. Policemen's truncheons are used as sudden tourniquets, a signal gantry is blown from the railway line to the street. At the Ritz all the cooking for some days is done on two up-ended electric radiators, in the garden of a House of Charity one garden seat is pulverized and its yard-away neighbour left lonely and unscathed. Jewellery from a newly bombed house is stolen before the dust has subsided, a Mayfair flat complete with butler is given to a bombed-out East-Ender who is thereafter frightened to go to bed, as is his usual habit, with his boots on. At Charing Cross Railway Station a linesman is found watering a row of flowers saturated through the night by fire-hoses, in the streets dressing-gowned women wearing saucepans as tin-hats hurry about with cups of tea. From the gas-stoves of Pimlico there spurts water pressed into the broken gas-mains from an incident high up in Hyde Park, a service is held in the ruins of a newly bombed church. The park in autumn is bright with little whitish incendiary fires where the previous year the mounds of autumn leaves were burnt, in a call-box a warden with a smashed jaw is trying to spit his message through to the Control. Pigeons find ready-made perches in fire-grates lining the exposed upward walls of vanished houses, Savile Row suddenly becomes a queer outdoor draper's establishment with rolls of cloth draped all over the street. A hand still holding an umbrella protrudes from the mid-morning debris of a leisurely pavement, the songs of the moment most sung in canteens everywhere are 'Roll out the Barrel', 'Bless 'em All' and 'The Quartermaster's Stores'. The bar of a public house used as a temporary mortuary is serving beer at eleven o'clock the next morning, a white cat remains faithful to the wreckage of its empty, abandoned home. A corpse strewn in the death-dealing glass gets up and proves to be an unscratched drunk, there is the smell of an oil-stove mixed with the smell of a gasless winter morning's breakfast—or no smell, or no breakfast. Big Ben chimes before the nine o'clock news, and echoing from that lofty tower come the gathered notes of the siren wailing fortuitously at exactly that broadcast hour.

So passed the Blitz.

PART TWO

CHAPTER I

THE CIVIL DEFENDERS

PROLOGUE

Civil Defence activities in Westminster may be said to have started in July of 1935—when an Air-Raid Precautions Sub-Committee of the General Purposes Committee was appointed. This action followed a general request to local authorities from the Home Office. And thus, in a precautionary manner, as was their meaning, those initials so reminiscent of the war years in British towns came into practical being—A.R.P.

From 1935 onwards the question grew in importance and extended its scope—as more was discovered of the practical problems involved, as the political situation deteriorated. At the close of 1937 some three-quarters of a year before the Munich crisis, the sub-committee became a Special Committee. Some months after the Munich pact, in May 1939, its duties were again extended and it was enlarged into the Civil Defence Committee. Then, four days before the outbreak of war, it became the Emergency Committee—and it was this that henceforth throughout the war was to determine the internal affairs of defence, shelter, and rehabilitation of people and things in the City of Westminster.

In essence, then, the Emergency Committee developed from the City Council, an elected body; so that the defence of the city and its citizens was in hands chosen by these citizens. The committee had strong authority over all the war condition of the city: the Ministry of Home Security defined the shape of what was permissible—in terms of manpower, material, Treasury aid to expenditure—and thereafter it was up to the Emergency Committee to plan and put into effect whatever it chose within the generality conceived by the Ministry. By its vision, its energy, and its will to construct and organize, such a committee may be judged. Some local authorities failed. Some show an otiose record. The Westminster Committee was to prove otherwise.

METHOD

The executive of A.R.P. was in the charge of a committee of ten members plus the Mayor. The practical officer in charge of services was the A.R.P. Controller, whose headquarters were situated at the City Hall, and who was, in fact, the Town Clerk. But it will be seen from the chart on page 199 that the intricacies of defence in its entirety extended beyond such a central internal executive. There had to be constant liaison and consultation with other authorities, and there were to be followed, on the highest national level, the guiding policies of the Home Office. The internal executive of the City's A.R.P. was thus harnessed to the greater machine of all London, forming its part of the Regional System. But within the City, and within general limits set by the Government, its operational control was on the majority of affairs absolute.

The working chart demonstrates better than could be written here the diverse organization. Liaisons were in many cases complicated. For instance, Police divisions coincided in no way with the City boundaries. There was not one, but there were three Fire Service areas to deal with. Two electric supply companies served different parts of Westminster, with an internal boundary within the City limits. However, against these diversities must be placed an experiment in centralization that was unique in Westminster—the system of maintaining four large Depots where the Council's First Aid parties and the L.C.C.'s Heavy Rescue parties and ambulances were concentrated together with extra formations like the mobile canteens run by the Women's Volunteer Service. These originally diverse elements were thus under the exact control of the Depot Superintendent working under orders from the general Westminster Control at the Report Centre. Thus the A.R.P. Controller had immediate command over (1) his Wardens' Service (2) the Casualty Services (3) the Council's own departments for the continuance of the City's welfare and progressive existence. Together with this, close co-operation was possible with L.C.C. institutions within the City, such as the Rest Centres formed for the transit of people recently bombed out.

The problems of the Emergency Committee were largely bound up with governmental policy, with such varying matters as the amount of manpower available at this or that time during the war, and the release of materials and equipment from the Ministry of Supply. Added to this was the whole question of finance. The majority of A.R.P. expenditure was the responsibility of the Government, though large sums were also to be disbursed by the Council itself; but it was not always possible to put a decision into effect until the Government's ruling had been obtained; though the risk was sometimes taken. In this respect the actual wealth of Westminster often allowed the Council to effect measures that perhaps a poorer borough might not have been able to afford. However, such wealth may fluctuate with conditions. And this became uneasily true at one point of the war, when income fell sharply with the drop in rents and rateable values determined by bombing and evacuation. Westminster then received a loan from the Government: later, as times improved, and as London filled to overflowing, the position was well recouped. Often, despite the dangerous financial times, the Committee took a chance when they wanted something done; they pledged themselves in advance of Treasury aid.

It may be apposite here to stress that the record of such a Committee depends largely on the individual qualities of its members and of its chairman or leadership. In this instance, the chairman was no inactive chief-of-staff. The conception of a chairman as a man conducting meetings is here false: the chairman of the Emergency Committee made it his business throughout the war to know and study in detail every detail of the field beneath his survey—he knew, for instance, every post and every shelter personally, not as a gross item on the multitudinous bill of his affairs. He was not content only to be the delegate of incoming news. Every morning the 'dawn patrol' set out to visit incidents. The chairman and reference members of the Committee made it their business to go too, to see for themselves, to study the needs of the man on the job.

DEVELOPMENT

In the following pages, each facet of the Civil Defence system will be studied as a separate entity.

Each service, each constructional necessity developed during the whole war according to its individual exigency. However, certain generalizations can be made, for experience and efforts towards greater or different efficiency naturally coincided with the momentum of the war in general. Such generalization is in no way absolute. Certain organizations were completed before others, while in several departments the time-lag became for various reasons greater. However, general tendencies may be noted.

Thus one may start with the initial gathering together of information as from 1935. Prophetic books were studied and balanced against the experience of the last war and later of the contemporary Spanish Civil War. An A.R.P. Training Centre was set up in 1936—the first of its kind in London. The idea of gas was much in men's minds and as early as this some 500 persons were trained in anti-gas precautions. Then, a general A.R.P. exhibition was arranged. In 1937 and 1938 A.R.P. lectures were given in Caxton Hall—and the inquisitive, half-apprehensive audience half filled it. Early in 1938 wardens were trained. So that generally a nucleus of knowledge was being formed through those years—and its development culminated first with the Munich crisis in the autumn of 1938.

At this time vigorous action was taken. There were, for instance, some 2,000 resident and some 2,500 non-resident wardens enrolled and in the course of training. In case of extreme need—the crypts of eleven churches were made available as temporary mortuaries. The first survey of basement shelters was already completed. Since not much building could be done in the time a force of 3,500 men were set to digging trenches in the Parks and squares (and here it may be noted in passing, and as a comment on the mixed feelings of the time, that those men engaged upon trench-digging in St. James's Park had to an extent to dissimulate their actions—just in case Herr von Ribbentrop might see a little and deduce too much from the balcony of the Embassy in Carlton House Terrace). By the time work was suspended (30th September) about a 20,000 foot run of trenches had been developed. In addition other necessary services had been assembled, such as rescue and demolition parties—then formed of building contractors' employees —and such as decontamination squads and first aid posts manned by St. John and Red Cross personnel.

So that, by the time of this emergency, the first nucleus had grown into an organized combative body, not perhaps of the strength needed to face a Wellsian offensive from the air, but nevertheless of energetic growth.

Thereafter, it was to be 'peace in our time'. But in March the bubble petered out—the Hungarians moved north into the Carpatho-Ukraine and Germany crossed into Czechoslovakia. The Italians chose Easter for a landing in Albania and on April 26th compulsory military training became the law in England. Then through the summer the acceleration of events towards war—and all this time the acceleration in London of air-raid precautions. Training was advanced, recruitment increased in tempo with anxiety.

THE CIVIL DEFENDERS

In the last days of August and those first two days of September came the final spurt. Sandbag filling was the order of the day in the parks, and a wholesale signing in of recruits went on at the mobilization points of the various A.R.P. organizations. Rescue, Wardens and First Aid services had to be brought up to full strength in a few days. The order went out to accept anybody. The important thing was to have as many hands available as possible. Those already trained would form the nucleus of knowledge around which this extra muscle would work. As it happened, the year-long lull afterwards changed the minds of many of these eve-of-the-war recruits and many left: the minds were also changed of the authorities towards certain of the less responsible elements, and these were caused to leave. But—as much was done at that time as could be. Britain was in most respects unprepared; there had to be a muddled sprint through those final hours of complacency; and if the expected armada had arrived on the 3rd, then it was just as well to have as many hands at work as possible. Even then, as the possible fury of attack was estimated, the strength of those 1939 services would have been inadequate. Tens of thousands of casualties were expected. It is doubtful how far civil defenders could have coped with such a situation. However, the attack never came. When on the Sunday morning of Mr. Chamberlain's announcement the sirens sounded for the first time in earnest and people cleared off the street and into their gas-masks— nothing happened. And nothing much more happened throughout that extraordinary winter and the spring. Except yet another stage in A.R.P. development—the first period of training on duty.

During the year between the Septembers much training was done; many of the personnel felt themselves to be useless and left; obligations elsewhere forced others to leave; but still others joined—and there was more training. So that this period combined a weeding out of both the more ambitious of those called elsewhere and of the least enthusiastic, while the main core settled down into their depots and posts and routines. Vehicles and equipment were progressively improved. And when the Luftwaffe came at last there stood to face it a body theoretically trained. Practically, this body did its job. But there was still room for revision and improvement.

Reorganization went hand in hand with experience through the Blitz. As in the field of battle, counter-measure followed measure. There was no stable moment. And when the Blitz was done there came the period of the long lull—which became the most intensive period of training and reorganization. Personnel was depleted by an increase in the age-limit of those conscripted for the army. But much of this was offset by a higher standard of training in the main body, and in improvements of procedure. So that, in 1944, when the Luftwaffe came again with its short but sharp raids and later with pilotless missiles, the Civil Defence organization stood at its most efficient pitch ever—and showed by the results a record of success.

That is the very general picture of the development of Civil Defence. Apart from their nights of action, officers and personnel will remember the war as a time of training, training, training; of exercise after exercise, of new technique after new technique to be learned. It never stopped. Often it continued during the active months; in some departments, every day. Now, in what historically was the 'Lull' period of 1941–1944, a period of two and a half years, there is a moment to examine individually the various elements of Westminster's wartime life—from wardens to the life on the river, from the gas engineer's problem to the running of the great Casualty Depots, from the fireman's life to life lived in the shelter.

First of all, that man-and-maid-of-all work, the warden.

THE WARDENS' SERVICE

The warden's first duty was the reporting of air-raid damage and the assistance of his brother services in their work of rescue and first aid. Otherwise, his responsibility knew no concise limit—for he was charged with the general welfare and comfort of the public during and after aerial attack. He had to be patient, understanding and responsible. He had to know much. He had to patrol the streets throughout raids and without the respite of cover between actions. He had to know most thoroughly his Post Area, and furthermore to have as correct an idea as possible of the habits of shelter of the people who lived there. He had to be technically trained in Incident Control, First Aid, War Gases, and the diagnosis of every type of bomb—from a Butterfly to a Parachute Mine—and of every type of street breakage—from a gas main to a sewer. He had to take part in special schemes, such as the watching of the Thames for mines and the action to be taken in the case of saturation raids or invasion. He became an authority, he had to *know*. His word was important—for it was the first word to get to the Control, and on it resided much of the decision as to what forces might be commanded to the incident. And this 'he' often meant 'she', for there were many women wardens; while some took telephonist duties, others patrolled on equal terms with the men.

The ordinary warden's view of the war was intimate. He was concerned with the necessities of a few streets—no more. In practice, Westminster was divided into five districts (plus the special area of Whitehall) which were then subdivided into some twenty-eight Posts. These posts were in turn divided into 250 sectors. The Post was the responsibility of each ordinary warden. It was up to him to maintain a census of the people sheltering and resident on his apportioned beat, it was his job to see that all the A.R.P. machinery of the street was in running order. And when a bomb fell, it was he who was first on the spot, and who then ran—or possibly cycled—to his Post to report the first news that would be telephoned then instantly through to the Westminster Control.

The service was manned by mixed whole-time and part-time personnel in varying complement at various periods of the war. For the first part of the war, and during the Blitz, wardens retained much of their civilian appearance, for their only uniform was a pair of blue overalls and a steel helmet. Later, they were issued with dark blue battledress and berets, as were other of the Civil Defence services. So that, on the cold winter nights of 1940–41, it was a common sight to see your warden muffled up in his own greatcoat, with a steel helmet the only sign of his freezing wardenship.

At times lack of personnel meant long patrolling hours, and part-time wardens who had been at work all day did much to mitigate the situation. It was a tiring stretch for them—a full day at the office or factory, and then an active night till dawn. Sometimes they would return for a second night, though this was dictated rather by enthusiasm than by necessity.

Apart from the general problem of keeping up to date a census of residents—a matter which varied from place to place with the type of co-operation given—there were perhaps two main problems for the wardens' service. One was the question of Whitehall, with its government offices and its security taboo on the admission of outside help. Each office maintained its own wardens' service. For this, the personnel available was slender; and there occurred a time-lag before any serious incident could be reported to the main Westminster Control, for the Whitehall offices had their own co-ordinating system based on the Ministry of Works. Later, after the Blitz, the position was reviewed, and while private staffs were maintained, the area came for all general purposes under the control of Westminster Civil Defence.

The second problem was a general one, not unique in Westminster. It was the question of Incident Control, or the creation of a system of absolute control by one man over all the services working on one incident. During the Blitz, incidents tended to become muddled for want of this co-ordinating officer. Sometimes the police controlled an incident, sometimes a warden or two wardens or perhaps an officer of the heavy rescue service took partial charge. In consequence of misunderstandings experienced—inexperienced officership, duplicated messages, unauthorized countermanding of messages—certain Incident Officers were trained from the Wardens' Service. These officers became highly specialized. At an incident they wore a pale blue helmet covering, and their position was marked by a blue light. This was the point henceforth from which the entire plan of campaign was organized. Police, the National Fire Service and all other Civil Defence personnel were directed from this centre. Under the officer's command, the Women's Voluntary Services set up Incident Inquiry Points; these satisfied the personal questions of residents and relatives, and proved an innovation of immense value.

Apart from the incidence of bombs a warden's life remained a busy one. They controlled, for instance, shelters. There were over seventy shelter wardens, and in addition a number of shelter marshals at the larger shelters. And in 1943 the public gas cleansing stations came also within the warden's province; here over fifty men were enrolled and trained in special duties. And apart from such front-line activities, many other jobs were undertaken during the quieter times—work such as the sale of coal from a dump set up by the Council against a severe winter. In 1944, for instance, wardens sold 103,781 tickets representing 648 tons of coal that could be taken away in small quantities by needy householders. They assisted thus in every way possible—in snow clearance, in toy-making for day nurseries, and in the assembly of small articles of war equipment to implement the general production drive of the last years.

However, those were supplementary jobs. The main work was done during raids: either in the heat of heavy bombing, or in the decaying hours of long and silent night patrol. The first work was the reporting and reconnaissance of an incident, the extinguishing of incendiaries, and the guidance of bombed-out people to shelter or rest. But practically the warden's record extends far, far beyond this. The history of the wardens' service is virtually a history of the whole perspective of the bombed streets. One cannot quite place the limit. They burrowed about in the dangerous wreckage, they risked fire and gas, they played with delayed action bombs, they administered to the wounded and generally were men and maids of all the work which in the following sections will be described. No more can be said than this—that among all the others, at any type of incident, there was likely to be the shadow of a warden working side by side with the mobilized expert. So the detail of much of the rescue and first aid and incendiary fire-fighting activities described in the following pages must be realized to refer *also to the warden's experience*.

THE HEAVY RESCUE SERVICE

The service was organized by the L.C.C., but directed in action by the Westminster Control. The men and their heavy lorries were attached to the four Westminster combined Depots.

As in all other services that were so quickly mustered in the first days of war, their number included men of all professions and of all types. Labourers, actors, con-men, clerks and even Germans made up their strength: but of these, the hard core were men of the building trade—for a knowledge of the ways of houses was an essential part of what almost became an intuition with these men. The first officers were surveyors and clerks of works. As time went on, the service—originally called the Rescue, Shoring and Demolition Service—was weeded and trained and strengthened and more fully equipped. But it retained in its character a roughness and an independence of spirit that was not so much evident in other groups whose work, though arduous, was in ways smoother and not so concerned with the material heaviness which was meat and brick to the Heavy Rescue man. From the days when they were first seen frying bacon on spades outside the Depot at Berkeley Square, to the later days of dark blue battledress, they developed their technique but retained still a buccaneering blend in their character. This had much to do with their task of reaching, through intractable masses of debris, people who were slowly dying and whose minutes depended upon the ruthless, though coldly sane action of the Heavy Rescue man. So, when they wanted something like extra equipment, they were not likely to beg for it: they 'borrowed' it. Once—and this will have happened on other occasions—one party needed an air compressor machine to get through to the buried wounded. They telephoned one of the utility companies, reporting a broken main and an urgent need for repair men with a compressor. It was a plain lie—to save time. They got their compressor. And they got out their wounded.

The Rescue Service was the only perfectly new service produced by the war. There had never been an equivalent of any kind, there had never been the need to study on such a scale the incidence of broken buildings upon trapped bodies. So, perhaps more than anyone else, they learnt as they went. They learnt how to walk on debris, carefully, so as not to disturb further the silting plaster and drown those beneath with dust. They learnt, working above ground, to use their hands or handshovels—these were more tender weapons than a pick or spade. They learned that sound travelled far under the earth. They learnt the ways of tunnelling, the stresses and strength of different types of debris. Under those newly fallen mounds of earth they learnt that such a thing as a spring mattress might block their way more emphatic-ally than a brick wall: the springs of the mattress wrapped themselves around their arms and the flock or feathers choked and blinded the little air there was. They learnt to listen for water, particularly for the dan-gerous and powerful gush of a hydraulic main rising swiftly under pressure. They learnt that a wet bandage over the mouth was useful when the smell of gas promised sudden thick pockets in the wreckage. But neither gas nor water deterred them, nor the tremendous weight that might at any moment collapse and inter them as thoroughly as the people for whom they were digging. These people, they learnt further, would often be found almost unwounded packed into some fortuitous crevice in the debris—beneath the angle of a propped up wardrobe, under a bed, in a corner beneath an obliquely collapsed ceiling. They developed a strange sensitivity in their burrowing through the slow plaster-ridden tunnels. They planned their direction first on the warden's census and the known habits of the buried; then on sound —calling and tapping for an answer; failing these, on the most likely places of shelter in the building; and finally—a phenomenon of either intuition or some re-awakening of urgent animal senses—there were some men, known within the service as 'the bloodhounds', who, through all the heavy odour of disintegrated plaster and brick, could smell human blood—and only, at that, *live* blood.

Often before beginning a rescue, when nothing was known of the position of those underneath, there would come one of the most pro-foundly moving moments of that time—the call for silence as rescue men tapped and called. Then all those standing free above the pressed-up mound would stop talking, turn off the engines of their vehicles, listen. The air whispered its anxiety, the silence strained. Those sounds from above, the droning planes and the anti-aircraft fire, became momentarily accentuated. But when they had passed, the silence closed in again with mineral tenacity, stifling, steely. One felt alone and lost above the pile of secretive rubble. Some people remember that they felt—peculiarly tall. And in the quiet the voice of the rescue caller echoed, repeated, echoed . . . so often with no reply. But reply or no reply, a decision would be taken, and nothing would stop these men until every possible chance of reaching a living person had been exhausted. And then they hated to leave the debris. When they knew definitely of the whereabouts of their quarry, either by a faint tapping or a muffled cry, they developed a hunter's attachment to success; and many a man who had been digging and tunnelling for hours would refuse to be relieved until he himself had performed the final rescue to which all his nerves and muscular tensions had for so long been devoted. They became used to handling the dead—to many the plaster dust was a relief, for it coated and thus dehumanized the skin of those poor ones underneath. They became used to it, but with one exception—the sight of the body of a child. This unsteadied for the next days the tried, tough composure of many who had never been shaken before.

Westminster presented one particular problem to the Rescue Service, the size and weight of many of its buildings. This meant that more people were liable to be trapped than at incidents in other boroughs, where the debris was usually lighter. It meant also that more concrete and stone slabs had to be negotiated. Special equipment was often called for; that was where the air compressor came in, and the Kango hammer, and cranes to lift the girders and blocks.

After the urgent moments of rescue, their job—or the job of the first daylight shift—was primary demolition and shoring. Buildings still standing had to be made safe—dangerous coping stones knocked down, sharp glass destroyed, walls and doors and windows strengthened with timber props. Then, more unpleasant, was the clearance of the dead. Often this meant some days of work, possibly until the whole site had been cleared; bodies would be decomposed, and special sanitary sprays were introduced.

Finally, rescue men were called upon—in their first capacity of men who would risk the collapse of a dangerous building—to the rescue not of people but of inaccessible furniture and effects, often a godsend to people who had overnight lost so much.

THE LIGHT RESCUE SERVICE
(Stretcher Bearers)

This corps, based on the Depot with the Rescue Service and the ambulances, was first conceived in terms of 'field stretcher parties'. Overalled and steel-helmeted, these men had the job of attending the exposed wounded on the spot, providing measures of first aid treatment, deciding which cases needed the ambulance and the hospital, and bearing such cases on their stretchers from the ruins or the street to the ambulances that accompanied them. They worked under any conditions, under concentrated bombing, through fires, in collapsing buildings, in the dark and under all weather conditions—and this specifically is mentioned here to indicate that their task of cool and swift diagnosis under such conditions was not an easy one.

They worked in parties of four men and a driver, using light cars carrying their stretchers and first aid equipment. However, it so happened that in the case of Westminster the high solid buildings took a strategic charge of the situation—so that often these men, though arrived speedily on the job, were forced to wait until the Heavy Rescue service had completed the long task of extricating the heavily trapped. But such nights were not nights for standing about, and naturally they learned to help as far as possible the Heavy Rescue services; and from this the idea developed of a Light Rescue service rather than a purely first aid party. In the long first year before the Blitz, they had received some training in light rescue work; the realization of conditions where most casualties were heavily trapped accelerated the change in the conception of their duties.

First aid on the spot was not over-elaborate, though casualties dealt with were mostly severe. Shock was usually present, and its sedative a matter of first importance; warmth and as soon as possible a warm drink were necessities immediate in the minds not only of these light rescue men, but also of all those wardens, police, home guard and others who had received training in basic first aid. Fortunately, severe bleeding was relatively uncommon, so that the dangers of the tourniquet were largely avoided. Darkness and the pasting over of dust often made diagnosis impossible on the spot—such wounds as fractures were difficult to diagnose or immobilize properly. What mattered most, and where these light rescue men succeeded, was the first treatment for shock and a rapid removal to hospital and proper medical treatment.

THE AMBULANCE SERVICE

The regular white ambulances of the L.C.C. were frozen and a fleet of auxiliaries was housed at the Westminster combined Depots to answer the Control's call to all air-raid incidents. White ambulances were retained to attend maternity cases and other normal accident and sickness casualties. So that here we must be most concerned with the newly formed auxiliaries.

In the first year training was, as with the other services, intensive. Though in the scramble of recruiting and equipping at the outset of the war they were provided with any available vehicle from a converted furniture lorry to a 'Ticky Snacks' van (in line with the taxis of the Auxiliary Fire Service and some of the rather odd vehicles that accompanied the British Expeditionary Force on its first crossing to France). Nevertheless by the time of the Blitz matters had been better organized. The new grey-painted auxiliary ambulances proved adequate for their work, high-powered saloon cars with new-built square van-backs equipped with stretcher rests and other necessities.

These cars, staffed with driver and attendant—for the most part women—drove out nightly to collect their wounded. Such feminine personnel were as new to the sight of wounding and the sounds of agony as any other of the civil defenders who came from so many different walks of life. They varied from working women used to hard things and the iron of life—to the leisured who had perhaps never before touched a bar of unperfumed soap. Now all these mixed up were thrown with the rest into the rubble, the cold, the gloomy bruising and killing. One girl who drove her ambulance car throughout the Blitz was physically sick every night at the sound of the sirens: yet she never missed a call. Theoretically, their job was to drive to the incident and carry away from there the wounded to hospital or to a First Aid Post. Practically, this involved driving through any bombing—perhaps in one of those earsplitting concentrated moments when the German planes seemed to have settled on one spot and no other—and then waiting out in the open while the casualties were being extricated. In those periods there was little to do—but wait, and listen, and think. Such enforced inactivity out in the open was perhaps the hardest of all experiences under fire.

Apart from air-raid action, ambulance auxiliaries attended certain war-conditioned accident calls. One night in Victoria there was a stabbing and shooting among some soldiers in the Station Yard; here a case of arterial bleeding called out the auxiliaries. On another occasion there was a row in a shelter. The ambulances were called—to find that their job on this night was to remove from the shelter somebody whose not unodorous presence was affecting the sleep of the others. And during the day, ambulance cars were used for all manner of conveyance—from the cartage of bread to hospitals to the delivery of mail and the transport of medical supplies. There was one celebrated morning when an ambulance car was assigned the task of conveying 'certain persons' from County Hall to a research station in Dollis Hill. This was naturally a special and important commission, such research workers were well in the secret list; and consequently the very best of the ambulances was despatched with the prima donna of all drivers at the wheel. At County

Hall the ambulance was opened, and the research workers, carrying a disquieting selection of buckets and brooms, took their places. A posse of charwomen.

An unforgettable ingredient in the texture of ambulance life was the word 'maintenance', the maintenance in perfect running order of their machines. This applied to all civil defence vehicles and their personnel, who spent their lives never far from the acrid smell of pink wartime petrol, and oil-cans, and buckets of washing water—but though the standard of all machines was kept as far as possible up to perfect pitch, the tradition of emergency underlying the ambulance idea seemed to demand a greater immaculacy of order and efficiency than any of the others, save perhaps the engines in fire stations. Life was thus lived in the midst of these contingencies, in the communal Depots, with the smells of dried concrete and the clothey camouflage nets that were later, in the lull, to become a part-time production work. The shifts were stabilized at twenty-four hours on and twenty-four off, in perpetual rotation. The active nights were spent out by the cold ruins in those thin blue cotton coats that served through the Blitz as a uniform; the days were spent in maintenance, cleaning, rest after the night, training and of course various recreation—from ping-pong to reading, and much of that most popular of all contemporary pursuits, the drinking of a cup of tea.

THE FIRST AID POSTS

These were of two kinds—static Posts and Mobile Aid Posts. They were both instituted to take care of those cases too severe for an ordinary patching up by wardens or at home—yet not grave enough to burden the hospitals. The fixed First Aid Posts were situated in the combined Depots and at Westminster Hospital, with an additional smaller post at the Soho Square Hospital.

There were as well many smaller private posts in office buildings and Government buildings, and in many of the larger shelters—but the six main Posts formed the kernel of the City's plan. However, though these were completely equipped and efficiently staffed, it was thought that the distances between them were so great that a system of mobile Posts was also evolved.

Five Heavy Mobile Aid Posts were put into service. They were quartered in the combined Depots, they responded to a call from the Control at City Hall. They comprised a large van with a driver and this was staffed with six auxiliary nurses, three orderlies, one trained nurse and a doctor (later, during the Lull, the complement was much reduced). Secondly, there were light units comprising a car with two Red Cross nurses, one trained nurse and a doctor. Their greatest use was found to be at those incidents where, for any reason, casualties were much delayed in their removal. Otherwise it was often the best course to avoid any delay and despatch the wounded straight to hospital —for however skilled the Mobile Post might be, it had nevertheless to work in limited conditions, and the delay of a few minutes taking a recently wounded person to hospital was preferable to possibly inadequate treatment under field conditions.

In a number of cases—at Great Peter Street, Garland's Hotel, Newport Buildings, etc.—a Mobile Aid Unit stood by for many hours while trapped casualties were gradually extricated. The interval between wounding and reaching hospital amounted often to many hours, and a short delay at the Post became therefore immaterial, affording sufficient resuscitation to make the patient fit to stand the journey to hospital.

Nurses and doctors worked under strenuous conditions. They had to attend casualties in the debris, trapped but accessible, and there do what was immediately possible. Mine dressings were much used—it was often the best thing to cover and immobilize a wound with these ready-made appliances, without disinfecting, without operation; and then get the patient away as quickly as possible to the warmth of a bed and considered treatment. Morphia injections were made, often through clothes when the casualty was only partly accessible. These things were done in the mud and plaster, in awkward crevices, in the incredible heaviness and sharpness and ubiquitous dirt of shattered houses. Sometimes doctors and nurses went crawling through tunnels after the rescue men, to tend perhaps for hours the exhausted buried lying wedged at the end of dark, dust-deciduous burrows beneath an enormous weight of masonry and brick pressing down from above. It was never as open as an operation on the battlefield. The complexities were endless—once a limb had to be amputated so that engineers could get at a broken water main that was endangering other lives. Then there was the undramatic but essential and extremely awkward necessity of getting liquid to the trapped person—to get a trickle of water or soda-bicarbonate through a rubber tube to a face not immediately accessible; or sometimes warm tea from a spouted enamel feeding-cup.

Bearing in mind the awkwardness of the terrain, it is interesting to picture the effect of a nurse's appearance in action. Unlike other women civil defence workers, she had not the option of trousers. She wore her nurse's uniform; over this a greatcoat; and over that a bleached calico apron; in the apron's three pockets dressings and other necessities; a steel-helmet, a torch, gum-boots, a gasmask, and swinging above all this a water-bottle.

Such then were the conditions of field-work. Often the most sensible course was to despatch the casualty to hospital or to one of the fixed First Aid Posts. One of the major virtues of these fixed Posts, and a first reason for their incorporation in the Depots, was that they were all underground and relatively safe. For the conscious patient, this provided the good sensation of refuge; for the medical staff, the conditions made for greater tranquillity in work which was best done without hurry and with all calmness. So the Depot posts were built into the great underground garages and basements of Kingston House, Dolphin Square, Berkeley Square House, and the flats of the Adelphi. This decision was made early, so that, in fact, when the Berkeley Square garage itself was first being built, water installations were laid in the concrete that later fed the First Aid Post. Another advantage was the ample floor space, and the good side entrances for access and egress of stretchers. In practice, it was found that on the whole air-raid casualties were either very severe or trivial—and that the intermediate class, with whom these First Aid Posts were primarily expected to deal, hardly occurred. However, many quite minor injuries and many persons who on further diagnosis were found to be only shaken and bruised were treated effectively; in this way the hospitals were protected from a large influx of such minor cases. But often, too, the opposite occurred, when faulty diagnosis at the incident sent very badly wounded stretcher cases to the Depots, cases that had thence to be sent to hospital. After attention at these Posts, the injured could spend the rest of the night in warm conditions in the rest-rooms attached; there they were given tea and the mental comfort of solid shelter and an emergency organization close at hand. Nurses on duty remember the many cases of splintered glass cuts that had to be attended to; the many casualties who were brought in with most of their clothes blown off; such dramatic entrances as the man who walked into the Kingston House Post with a large splinter of wood sticking out of the top of his head like a dagger.

Around this central hub of the First Aid Posts stretched the multitudinous affairs of the Depot general. At the Berkeley Square Depot, for instance, there would be some two hundred and thirty personnel on duty at one time—a mixed lot from Heavy Rescue men to these nurses, from ambulance drivers to Light Rescue men and to the Women's Voluntary Services. Blue overalls, dark blue uniforms with yellow flashes, the white and grey and red-crossed nurse's dress, the green tweed of the Women's Voluntary Services—all these made up the scene in the canteen where staff from the Mecca cafés served out meals. There, or in the dormitories or out with their machines they waited during raids for the warning bell that heralded a call-out. Then messengers would come from the Depot Superintendent's Watch Room with orders for specific squads to get mounted and off. There would be a roaring of engines, a clattering of steel helmets, and then, for a few minutes afterwards, a kind of vacuum. Nobody ever quite knew who was going to come back, and who was not.

But then the piano would start up again, or the darts would flutter, and not much more would happen until the next bell rang, or the first blooded casualties came in, or—as sometimes did happen—the whole place, underground as it was, suddenly dissolved into chaos from the blast of a nearby bomb. In this regard, two Depots were once hit and temporarily put out of action at the same time: a concentration of calls were made on the other two Depots by the Report Centre, but fortunately these satisfied all immediate necessities; if that had not been possible, then external aid from other boroughs would have satisfied, with not much of a time-lag, the needs of the night.

THE POISON GAS SERVICES

Poison gas was an obsession with pre-war strategists. Their prophecies were never fulfilled: though they were valid, for this was no psychological obsession, and stocks of enemy gas found since the capitulation have proved how real was the danger. Throughout the war, these services and installations first prepared were kept actively alert, and in cases even expanded.

The arrangements fell into seven main heads: personal protection (gasmasks); gas identification; decontamination of streets, buildings and vehicles; cleansing of gas-infected clothing; the issue of bleach cream, the cleansing of the public and treatment of gas casualties.

Many thousands of black rubber respirators were issued to civilians and their children, over a thousand specially contrived helmets were provided for babies. Civilians were encouraged to carry these wherever they went, and it was usual to see on the streets the cardboard box containers dangling from an arm, or more elegant boxes and bags in various materials manufactured for the ladies. At times, gas practices were suddenly imposed on crowded streets. Tear gas was used. Those who had forgotten their masks were given a crying reminder not to do so in future.

Gas identification officers were recruited from local analytical and pharmaceutical chemists, supplemented by other volunteers who acted as their assistants. In the event of a gas warning, they were required to attend the virulent area in a specially equipped van, then to confirm the presence of gas, recognize its type, determine the area of poisoning and generally advise on the tactics of decontamination. They worked on a rota, unpaid. Although on several occasions they investigated false alarms, circumstances never demanded their services in full action. However, they and other personnel of the anti-gas services had to remain on duty constantly and participate in exercise and training schemes. They were not, in fact, as idle as their calling suggests.

A large personnel was trained in flushing, dusting and sweeping gas-smirched streets: others specialized in the decontamination of vehicles, for which there were allocated certain weathering parks; yet others were prepared for the collection of contaminated debris, the running of mustard laundries and other duties necessitated by the pervasive, noisome, persistent presence of liquid gas from which as much as possible had to be restored immaculate.

Installation of mustard-gas laundries, gas-cleansing stations, and ventilation systems and gasproof doors in official buildings involved much thought and expense. Arrangements were made from a network of chemists to provide bleach cream for persons contaminated with mustard or lewisite gas: many hundredweights of bleach powder were distributed. Posters advising various gas precautions were to be seen everywhere, yellow notices directed the gas-wounded to the nearest cleansing stations, and a sign of the possible times were strange boards and the tops of pillar boxes painted with a pale green as poisonous in appearance as the gas it was designed to detect.

THE FIRE SERVICE

The Fire Service was not nationalized until the summer of 1941. During the Blitz it was organized by the L.C.C. It maintained its own systems of areas and districts, without regard for City or Borough limits, so that Westminster was served by the London Fire Service as a whole, with of course a tendency to utilize those stations and concentration points nearest to fires.

On Westminster territory there were two regular stations—the Shaftesbury Avenue station that was bombed and then rebuilt, and

The Swimming Pool at Buckingham Palace

At the Royal College of Surgeons

Nuns in Claverton Street

St. Clement Danes Church, Strand

House in Lowndes Square

Rescuers at work on the printing works in Peter Street

Sheltering in the Aldwych Tube

The plume of the Aldwych Flying-bomb

The Aldwych Disaster

Aftermath at the Aldwych

the station in Horseferry Road. The small grey trailer pumps and heavy fire units supplied to the L.C.C. by the Home Office were housed with their numerous auxiliary personnel in schools and other vacated buildings with parking space and accommodation; these were called sub-stations, and were spread round the regular stations in numbers of about five to a station. Auxiliary fire stations were, for instance, situated in a garage and mews off Park Street, and at Westminster School. The tour of duty was more onerous than in other civil defence formations—it stood at forty-eight indivisible hours of duty and then twenty-four hours of leave. This had the effect of concentrating life more at the station than at home, and semi-military discipline was aimed at; or rather, semi-naval, for the jargon of a fire station and much of the atmosphere is of the sea, a legacy of the regular firemen, who are mostly retired navy men. In addition to whole-time auxiliaries there were many part-time volunteers.

In their dark-blue uniforms with silver buttons and red piping, the new recruits spent a first year of teething much as did the other civil defenders. Their equipment was to hand from the very start, pumps and hose and ropes and ladders and strange coupling pipes of innumerable shapes and sizes. This intricate machinery took some study. Exercises were held daily; London grew used to seeing convoys of squat grey pumps drawn by taxis careering down the street in search of a fictitious fire—for following the precedent of Paris and the Marne a quarter of a century before, the taxicab was once more pressed into service in the first scramble for trailer-vehicles.

When they fought at last their first fires, the new firemen found them very different from their neat exercises. To begin with, they got wetter than they had ever thought a man could be. Fire is a dry element, but the fighting of it with water soaks the fireman to the skin in the first five minutes. Often then, in the cold of that winter, he was called upon to fight, wet and frozen, for a stretch of some fifteen hours without respite. Throughout this time he was the special target of the high explosives that were sent down to stir up the fire; he could not think of cover; the nature of the job kept him out in the open or up against the fire. It is, too, a particular tradition with London's firemen that they should attack the fire first from *within* the building—not from the safer ground outside. This was done whenever possible. Thus, many of the hours of bombardment were spent enclosed with the dark smoke and the fire between walls dangerously unstable, vulnerable both to the heat of the fire and the shaking up of a nearby bomb. There is no photographic record of this side of a fireman's experience: smoke makes it impossible: the pictures one sees of firemen out in the street show only half of the operation.

Westminster set its local problems, primarily in several large ware-house fires, in fires at factories such as the Palmolive works, and in the safeguarding of national buildings. But whatever the nature of the fire —whether it was complicated by burning oil or by a high wind and driving embers—the basic experience was the same. The fireman was drenched and physically exhausted. Apart from any gymnastics on high ladders and precarious roofs, there were always two constant burdens on his strength; one was the weight of all fire-service equip-ment, which is built as heavy as the heavy weather it is designed to withstand—all the glittering brass weighed solid pounds of brass, all those snakes of hosepipe were hard, concentrated canvas of whipcord durability; and the other burden was the water pressure, for the ejection at speed of concentrated water-gallons through an inch-wide nozzle kicked back like a team of mules. On the whole, not so much ladder-work was necessary as in ordinary peace-time fires; fewer people stayed in the upper floors of buildings, there was in comparison not the need for much high-level rescue; though, of course, this did occur on occasions. On the other hand, there was a great use of 'water-towers', the steel turntable ladders that extended to a height of one hundred feet from their mounting and bore aloft a fixed hose with a man to direct his jet. These were regular Fire Brigade machines, though in cases manned by specially trained auxiliaries. The height of West-minster buildings made a necessary call on them.

Apart from the concentration of high explosives unloaded around him, the fireman's greatest danger was not so much an encirclement by fire as the collapse upon him of the building itself. In the tremendous heat of even a small fire, the various materials used in the construction of the building will react in different ways. Steel girders ribbing a solid concrete floor will buckle and split the concrete; different formations of brick will give suddenly at weak points; timber supports will burn, and their decay will crack the floors above; small masonry but heavy as a cannon-ball will drop suddenly from a cornice or from the blazing rafters. Add the darkness inside, the heat that turns a hose-jet to steam, the smoke that peppers his lungs so that the fireman bends down on the nozzle where a draught of pure air magically breathes round the water-jet—add then to these normalities the unpredictable, the live electric cable and the bottles exploding in the heat like machine-gun fire, the sudden flare-up of petrol or spirit, the thousand other oddnesses of the lunatic experience of fire: lastly add the sudden deflation of the hose as the main outside is broken by high explosive, the wresting from him of the fireman's only safeguard, his water.

The provision of emergency water was without any doubt inadequate. There were firefloats on the Thames, and emergency hose-laying lorries to conduct water from these floats miles inland: but there were not enough of each. There were systems of relay pumping on land, from a good main to a dry area. But there were no deep-lift pumps on the Thames bridges, no second system of street pipe-mains whose fracture could be mended quickly by mobile engineers. There were certain water-tanks and other static supplies, but not the batteries of dams and tanks that in time came to infest the London street-scene. All these systems were completed by the National Fire Service during the long lull of 1942 and 1943.

FIREWATCHERS AND FIRE-GUARDS

In support of the Fire Services there lingered and grew and finally became systematized into an organized force a vast army of private and semi-public fire-fighting citizens. The history of this body, which began with pre-war governmental advice on the purely home fire that should not be kept burning, and which ended in a comprehensive and trained army of citizen fire-guards, is one which illustrates well the difficulties of placing a burden of duty upon the private citizen, without discipline, without a rigid and comprehensive scheme, without the encouragement of sufficient equipment and such aids to glory as a uniform.

The first appeal to reason was not a success. In many quarters much was faithfully done—but on the whole matters were neglected. There were reasons without number—such as the lull-year before the raids, with its apathies and its final fascinated disbelief in disaster; also the fact that many civilians during the raids were already engaged in active part-time work, in the Home Guard and in various other kinds of civil defence; and the fact that there was lacking an energetic stimulus from administrative quarters otherwise engaged. The tale of development is too complicated to follow here in detail, for it involved many stages of organization, schemes, circulars, promulgations. However, in general, the story follows certain practical stimuli administered by the Luftwaffe.

In the first months of the Blitz, local fire-fighting was a matter of local initiative. Wardens encouraged and trained householders, and there were formed street-parties. It is interesting to note, in this respect, that a plan of fire-guards organized in 1940 by a warden on the Mill-bank Estate very closely resembled the official Fire-Guard Plan insti-tuted by the Ministry of Home Security some three years later, even to some of the verbal designation employed. Many business houses also provided fire-guards, but the coverage of a concentration of important buildings such as existed in Westminster was not by any means ade-quate. Many fires occurred that later, when matters were fully organ-ized, could have been quickly extinguished. It was on the 9th December that a dropping of incendiaries heavier than usual gave the Council the idea of initiating a chain of fire observers to cover the whole of Westminster. This plan was put into operation, but during its recruit-ment the great fire-raid on the City of London occurred on the 29th December—and the Government ordered compulsory firewatching of all business premises.

But it was a long business, the circularizing of firms and the exam-ination of schemes for each premises. There was a lack of personnel available, there were disagreements about forming blocks (incorporating natural firebreaks) rather than purely individual schemes per premises. Then again the Luftwaffe took a hand, and with the experience of the April and May raids it was realized that more effective measures must be taken. A Fire Prevention Department was set up by the Council, and block schemes were organized for business areas; in residential quarters, the wardens' 'Neighbours' ' fire parties also had to be in-creased. So in Westminster a *compulsory* registration of male residents was effected. To illustrate the great difficulty of dealing with such a private population, this registration produced 10,000 registered persons, of whom no more than 2,000 were prima facie liable for enrolment; the rest were exempt. Later other enrolments produced similar results. So that by August 1942, after a generally unsuccessful drive for volunteers, the enrolment of women was made compulsory. At that time also, compulsory training was ordered for all fire-guards, as they were hence-forth called. But private removals and the drain of personnel into the Armed Forces and other duties of war still vitiated the scheme—so that at no time were there more than 700 fire-guards available per night in street parties, of which number many were even then called upon for duty in business premises.

In the spring of 1943 the situation was made more rational by the institution of the Fire-Guard Plan. This was the final phase. The City was divided up in ninety-eight sectors, subdivided into blocks and areas, and a personnel of some 6,800 fire-guards per night was trained. In the first three months of 1944, the plan operated—though unofficially. It was a success. In July 1944 it received official recognition. But then, as the chances of war decided, it was never afterwards operated.

The night-life of the individual firewatcher during the Blitz was often inactive, sometimes tempestuous, always tense and nerve-straining. On his duty-nights he had to be in or near the building of his watch by dusk. If there was no alert, then he could pass the hours as he liked— over a game of darts with other firewatchers, over the paper and the cup-of-tea—and then sleep on some improvised bed. If the sirens sounded, then he had to be up at his post on the roof. There, lonely among the roofshapes, high above the dark streets, he would wait and watch for the incendiary that might drop its feathery whistle on to his particular roof. Then there would be a clambering about with sandbags, or long-handled shovels, or buckets and a stirrup pump; he had a good chance of killing the bomb and its bright glare if he got there quickly enough; and if not, then he would be shouting to the street or sending down a message for assistance. But if no bomb fell, his would be the tedium of standing on those exposed heights throughout the night of objects from the air, with a perspective of other fires, within those few yards up a feeling of greater proximity to the falling bombs, with the drone of diving planes accelerating straight towards his ear and the livid yellow flashes and flares startling the roofscape into disquieting relief. In a world of collapsing buildings, the sensation of being at a height became doubly insecure; cover, steel-shod or bricked, seemed more fragile among the rooftiles (though in effect, when a house was brought down, it was often the people on the roofs and in upper floors who were safest—often they came down still capping the debris as it folded to the ground). So that in vertiginous and mentally exposed positions they watched throughout those tense nights, and according to each one's individual resources of sensitivity their achievement may be compared, for better or often for much worse, with the more active pursuits of the street.

THE POLICE

The Metropolitan Police Force built round its regular corps an auxiliary body of war reserve police. These were further supplemented by part-time special constables. The force owed allegiance to the Home Office direct, and as with the Fire Service conducted itself less with regard to City and borough boundaries as with its own system of divisions. In surveillance of Westminster, its chief operative stations were the new central station in Savile Row, the station by Scotland Yard, the Bow Street Station and that at Gerald Road. When Savile Row was bombed, Marlborough Street was used as the central west end station.

The life of the individual policemen during air-raids was, if not necessarily less unhappy than others, certainly a more uncertain one. Like the warden, the constable had a general job, and his was even less specific than the warden's. In theory, he was not so much a unit of civil defence as a defender of the peace, and as such and with the peace so much more shattered than at normal times, his duties were necessarily multiplied and complicated. He retained his normal functions of traffic control, movement of the public, and the preservation of order. But in excess of this, he was often found doing the work of a warden, a fireman, a rescue worker, a man of all first aid. Since he was out on the streets patrolling, he was often the first on the job, concurrently with the warden. When at an incident the first message had been telephoned or dispatched to the Report Centre, the natural act of a man on the street was to get into the trouble and help get those already inside out; the policeman was no exception. He was trained to take risks, he was trained in first aid and other ancillary needs. If an unexploded bomb fell, he saw that people within the danger area were evacuated to rest centres or shelters, and naturally he attended to the necessary diversions of traffic. If a bomb fell in a road, he reported the crater and arranged the traffic's alternative route. At some incidents in the Blitz the police worked as incident officers; but this was properly the responsibility of wardens, and finally ordered as such.

Londoners were celebrated for 'taking it', and in fact quite a number took as much as they could immediately lay their hands on; so the policeman was also on the watch for looters. Looting was not uncommon, was by all standards criminal and had to be stopped. Though no excuse can be made for it, its sudden motive can be found less in deliberate intention than in the somersaulting of all conditions of order in a destroyed area, in the proximity of so much that was broken and lost to some seductive article fortuitously untouched; that, and a greater awareness of the present rather than the future. It was a stain on the human character rather than on London's own. The police mounted guard over these temptations; or saw to it that members of the Home Guard stood on watch. This was a difficult, unpalatable job—when so many constructive matters of communal good needed attention.

Otherwise, the policeman's beat was troubled by many by-products of the war. By the black-out, and its covering up of what might otherwise not have occurred; by the black-out's increase of small accidents; by such frivolities as the Irish bomb-throwing of 1940; and by other eccentricities of the abnormal moment. Against this, his life was made rather happier by the emptier late-night-streets, by the decrease in traffic, and by a certain tendency of people to plague one another less and keep their own order more.

WOMEN'S VOLUNTARY SERVICES

Westminster owes much to these women exempt from conscription who volunteered, unpaid, to give extra help wherever necessary and whenever possible. Regularly, in hours and sometimes days and nights put aside from their household and other duties, they attended canteens or clothing stores, British Restaurants or hostels. They drove mobile canteens out into the worst steel weather, when the fire was at its fiercest. They manned Incident Inquiry Points during the Little Blitz and the flying-bomb period to come, they set their tables up on streets blooded and among scenes that would have been harrowing to soldiers and trained nurses.

In daylight they canvassed for salvage, repaired the bindings of books to be sent overseas to the Forces. They did all those small jobs that listed now look dull but were of such infinite decoration to the bare lives of many people then—helping the Local Information and War Savings Committees, knitting, organizing a children's clothing exchange, garnishing camouflage nets, distributing to air-raid victims gifts of furniture and clothes. Taken by and large, their main functions could be summed up as caring for the homeless, caring for the comfort of the services, and running such needful institutions as the British Restaurants.

They were organized. They had administrative leaders, but no officers, no discipline but their own sense of good order. Their activities in Westminster were run from the Edwardian block of luxury flats called Gloucester House. This millionaire's residence was turned into a hostel for the bombed out and the ground floor became the main British Restaurant in Westminster. The Women's Voluntary Services worked hard to organize this huge concern, and while they worked it was the bombed-out East-Ender who received the benefit of the sunken baths in the gorgeously tiled bathrooms. The restaurant, called the St. George's, was set up initially for the homeless, but gradually became a large-scale establishment that served three meals a day for many hundreds of people and whose food was so good that wealthy people staying at luxury hotels were known to come in for their bob's-worth. This Gloucester House was the hub, but otherwise the Women's Voluntary Services ran between forty and fifty other hostels.

Besides the background work of caring for so many individuals who had lost so much, and caring for them with understanding as well as with material comfort, there were many unexpected complications—the fact that ordinarily convalescent cases came to the hostels, that there were some old people too fat to sleep on an ordinary bunk, that despite their plight people retained their individual obsessions and brought them to the hostels—like the elderly woman whose delight it was to primp for long periods up and down the dormitory clad only in her barest underclothes, to the scandalized discomfort of those other ladies present. There were cases of diphtheria and tuberculosis to be contended with. There were times, too, of pressed urgency, when for instance 250 people arrived suddenly in the first week-end of the flying-bomb period.

Members of the service manned six canteens and one mobile kitchen. These served through the Blitz, going to where there were the largest concentrations of civil defence workers and therefore to the worst incidents. They worked long hours; on 16th May, for instance, Mobile Canteens were out on the job from 2 a.m. until 11 p.m. the next day—feeding as many as 15,000 people.

Women volunteers played their part in the special schemes for coastal evacuation and crash raiding—and here matters were organized down to the last tin-opener. They were in charge of billeting and caring for Belgian refugees who arrived in May 1940, taking them from the Guildhouse in Eccleston Square, which served as an assembly point and rest-place, to their billets in the district looking, as one report states, 'very odd as we set off, bicycles, prams, baggage, birds in cages, babies and Belgians'.

And finally these women, dressed in their familiar forest-green tweeds with dark red trimmings, brought an immensely variegated war service to a conclusion by taking over the vital Enquiry Points during the Little Blitz and at the large-scale flying-bomb incidents, setting up their books—in rough and unready conditions—on an orange box in the snow outside a bombed theatre, in a guardroom at Wellington Barracks, in a room used also as a temporary mortuary with the sacks of remains lying against the wall.

REPORT AND CONTROL CENTRES

When the warden's post telephoned its message through to the Report Centre, the words were received in a large basement room in the City Hall, at a desk of telephones, in an atmosphere of charts, maps, tallies, papers, concentration and calm toneless electric light. The Officer-in-Charge of the Centre was supported by a staff of telephonists, messengers and other officers including the City Engineer, the Medical Officer of Health, the Director of Public Cleansing, the Chief Warden and the District Rescue Officer, either in person or represented by their liaison officers. The operational headquarters of the A.R.P. Controller and his Deputies was located at the Report Centre, so that in all the Officer-in-Charge was able to consult immediately representatives of all services on the highest level.

The function of a central control was to receive and co-ordinate all messages from outside sources and either order out necessary services or pass on information to other authorities. Casualty and rescue services, mobile canteens, Gas Identification and Bomb Reconnaissance Officers, mortuary vans and other council units were ordered direct from this minute-to-minute planning board. Reinforcements were asked for from the next level—Group—and conversely reinforcements were sent to render assistance to other Boroughs; and both Group and Regional Headquarters were kept informed of all major developments. On the heavy nights, such as 16th April, as many as 200 parties were sent from outer boroughs in to the aid of Westminster. Westminster returned the compliment on several nights—often in terms of relief parties to areas whose own services were exhausted overnight. Besides this, all authorities external to the Council had to be informed of those matters that affected them. The Police had to know of all incidents and the position of unexploded bombs. The Fire Service were given calls for assistance and informed of the damage of water supplies. Damage was reported to telephone, gas, electricity, water and power undertakings, to the Ministry of Works and other government departments, to parallel local authorities, to railway and transport and all other appropriate organizations.

This work involved the reception and despatch of an immense number of messages—on each of two nights the Centre handled during the raid period over three thousand messages—an average of well over four hundred messages per hour. To deal with such a stream, and to avoid any dangers of clogging, decisions had to be made swiftly, and a system organized that would be both fast and foolproof, revealing as it went the changed situation. Thus conduits for the messages were fixed from telephonist to messenger to Officer-in-Charge to planning board to outgoing telephone system. On this circuit special forms were used, and a tally board registered visually the disposition of forces then at their stations or out at incidents. It was a device of split seconds, and one that had at the same time to follow Mrs. Beaton's important advice—'Clear as you go.' The mobile position as it changed from minute to minute had to be stated, freshly, concisely, uncluttered by the past.

Though this often white heat continued for long periods during raids, while the redder glows were firing the skies unseen above, while once the fire itself burnt furiously close in the rooms directly above—this was not the only work of the Centre. There was never a night, even during the Lull, when the Centre had not to deal with some contingency. For its function as a clearing house for civil defence activities of any nature had to continue. It had always to deal with such matters as furniture removal, mobile baths, emergencies arising at shelters, calls for accident and illness, infringement of black-out regulations, rest-centre arrangements and altogether a multitude of inquiries and reports on all matters relating to Civil Defence. Consequently, the room was manned on a twenty-four hour basis throughout the war; and there were reserve centres equipped and semi-staffed—one in the basement of the Buckingham Palace Road Library and a secondary reserve established (later in 1943) at Berkeley Square. This was the staff tent upon which all operations depended; no chances could be taken.

The Control Centre reported to Group Control and from here assessments of the situation were sent to Regional Headquarters—which was in fact housed in the Geological Museum near the Kensington Boundary. There the mobilization was conducted of all the forces in the London Region (roughly London and the Home Counties). But it would be extraneous to investigate here the function of this centre—though some idea of its more comprehensive duties may be obtained from a brief description of its superior, the Home Office War Room. This was the summit of the hierarchy of control centres and rose—or rather fell—some thirty feet at the Rotunda built near Millbank.

From street level this stronghold looks like a low, circular pillbox of immense proportion and constructed of thick concrete. On its dark flat roof the seagulls strutted in the winter, finding a beached solace in the pebbles laid there against incendiary attack. But beneath a dramatic edifice burrowed its way down into the earth, an arrangement of passages and offices and chartrooms, lit throughout by whitish-greyish fluorescent bars that are indeed a kind of daylight, the bleakest February daylight. This cylinder of concrete was built in the foundation pit of an ancient gasometer, and here for the latter part of the war were conducted the affairs of civil defence in co-ordination with Fighter Command, with key intelligence of factory dispositions and the placing of stocks of food, with intelligence of the results of German bombing that was forthwith used in reverse by Bomber Command in its strategy over Axis territory.

The Rotunda staff would have been protected and self-contained in the event of a temporary occupation of the ground above by parachute troops. Operations could have continued under a poison gas attack. It was a stronghold, concrete, air-conditioned, artificially daylit, stocked with the necessities of a siege, a modern place whose passages were lined with grey pneumatic tubes and with grey cables, and in whose depths there was set a steel door opening on to the almost un-mentionable underground tunnel connecting with . . . one cannot quite be sure.

CHAPTER II

THE SHELTERS

Shelters improvised deep in the circular waterwell of an iron-clad Victorian gasometer pit, in the long worm of tube stretching from the Aldwych, in the subterranean tiled flue of an electric power station, in the bright-lit concrete basement of a modern office-building, in a church crypt recently cleared of ancient bones, in cleared-out coal vaults, in trenches dug beneath the trees of railingless squares, in deep tube-railway stations busy with trains, in basements rooted with new struts and girders, in the macabre arches of Hungerford Lane, in such good buildings as the Central Hall and in such deathtraps as the Treasury, in a giant Green Line garage where groups of shelterers knew each other by the names of the old divisions of the old routes—Tadworth and Reigate—and, not improvised, the brick and concrete street shelters that in time rose throughout the streets like long, windowless, secret conveniences. These typify the private and public, the usual and unusual shelters that honeycombed the sieged City. There were other shelters too, and on the whole popular ones—any sudden archway; or the horizontal position assumed with alacrity against the face of the pavement or in that welcome declivity between the kerb and the roadway; and last, and physically the least protective, though not psychologically—one's own bed.

But here the more public shelters must be considered. The provision of these was the City's responsibility, and came mostly within the province of the Engineer's department; above this, questions of broad policy, intelligence as to the enemy's tactic, the release of necessary constructional materials and part of the finance involved were a matter for the decision of the Ministry of Home Security.

From the City's point of view, the practical story begins with an extensive study of the results of bombing during the Spanish War.

Then, in 1938, officials visited Berlin, other German cities, and Paris—to discover what they could of shelter development. At the hurried time of the Munich Crisis, trenches were dug in the parks and some squares. In 1939 these were extended, and lined and roofed with concrete. Before the outbreak of war, these trenches would have accommodated 17,000 shelterers.

During the first four months of 1939, a complete survey was made of all basements in Westminster. The 13,200 buildings embraced were then arranged in groups according to their permeability—and decisions were made as to the most suitable for public shelter. Sketch plans of protective works were carried out, negotiations were opened with owners and occupiers of the premises now scheduled. Then, in July 1939, the Civil Defence Act provided legislation necessary for requisition. Between July and September there was not time for much building to be done—and so the Government abandoned temporarily the idea of constructing special shelters and gave its blessing to the requisition of those premises selected by the City Engineer. Already, before the outbreak of war, the City had gone to work—and the first protective measures of sandbag blast walls, covered pavement lights and timber stall-boards had been erected—to the tune of some 85,000 sandbags and considerable quantities of timber.

Thus on the Sunday morning that began the war it was possible for the Council to run up posters all over the City advising the nearest shelter for a total of 51,000 people. That was an achievement in the time—the Engineer's Department worked day and night to spurt the job to a finish; but it was only an initial stage in what was to be throughout the first years of the war a constant development.

In addition to communal public shelters, it was the responsibility of the City to provide shelters for persons of small income. The Government designed the Anderson shelter for this purpose and later the Morrison table shelter. But both of these were unsuitable in any bulk for the Westminster terrain—the Andersons needed at best gardens, and buildings were on the whole too heavy for table shelters to be safe. Only 235 of the first, and 210 of the latter were ever installed. However, a successful alternative was found—in the vaults under the pavement opposite each house. The need affected mostly the Pimlico district, and here some 8,000 erstwhile coal cellars were cleared and appointed as shelters. They were provided with lighting, and communication gaps were knocked in the joining walls to provide an alternative passage of exit. This was, of course, not all effected overnight. But finally householders with such cellars were equipped with one of the safest and most convenient forms of shelter in London. From the Council's point of view, the risk of mass injury by a direct hit was spread, the sanitary problems reduced. For residents, there was the feeling of being near home, more or less private, and comfortable. One picture of such a vault shelter is remembered—its walls washed pink, real bedsteads installed, the electric light shaded, and a well-protected landlady surrounded by her brood of lodgers. By and large, there was only one rift in the general lute of these shelters—that since the lights were fed free off the mains, there was a little tapping done. Electric fires bred themselves rather too freely; but that was a little thing.

In company with other private shelters in business houses and other buildings these vaults were eventually opened to the general public—though they were little used in this way. This was a decision of the Council for the communal good, the result of a special request to the Government and an almost unique action.

Otherwise, Westminster's shelter situation differed from that of other boroughs in three main aspects—that the City was normally composed of a greater number of heavier and safer buildings than in other places, that there lay underground a greater concentration of deep tube stations, and that against these assets the floating population placed upon the streets the necessity of providing for a considerable space of temporary refuge.

There was a greater tendency for people to prefer deep and populous shelters to the bleaker surface buildings. It is now a well-proved fact that London was ill-equipped with deep shelters, and that only these could provide for a people strained with years of war-time living the proper psychological comfort—in fact, the rest at night that seemed for a spell *absolutely* secure, an *absolute* retreat. The other need for the company of others in time of danger is a familiar herd instinct, uplifting to the morale (if its seed is good) but dangerous from the practical points of concentration and the unlucky bomb. However, in the case of the tubes, there was relative safety. At peak sheltering times, as many as 4,000 people sheltered in the Piccadilly station. And the converted Aldwych line catered in its most populous moments for as many as 2,000 sleepers.

The Aldwych shelter was unique. Opened on 22nd October 1940, it comprised the actual Aldwych station and part of the tube itself running towards Holborn. At first—and it must always be borne in mind that the conveniences for sheltering for the night rather than for a small period were slow to develop—at first people slept everywhere along this disused line on the platform, in the passages, on the stairs, even in the 'suicide' pit alongside the electric rail itself. Then, in time, wooden railway sleepers were packed in to make a floor, and the length of tunnel was concreted and painted white. A First Aid Post was installed (this worked at full pitch throughout the Lull, people made it a sort of social centre for imaginary complaints), a canteen served hot snacks and tea, and on several occasions there were held concerts in which well-known theatrical personalities took part and which were broadcast by the B.B.C. Divine services were held on Sundays.

Special flood-gates were installed, for the tube was near the bed of the Thames; an air-conditioning system and a compressor-ejector sewage engine were operated. Filled with those many hundreds of people, the tube appeared less claustrophobic than it might usually do, though its cylindrical shaft looked and felt much narrower than one would imagine from the inside of a train. Although the din of barrage and bombing was hardly heard at that depth, there were other sounds busying from the earth pressing against those tunnel-sides—the gurgling of water in the sewers, the rumble of the post-office railway traversing somewhere near, sounds that suggested an intricate life proceeding in an earth that was not therefore so lonely. And over all this, over the bunks and the sleepers, there often crept a mist that diffused an added strangeness to the subterranean air, a light haze that suggested a gaslit London, which threw an unreal veil over the peace-time theatrical posters that remained throughout the war telling of other times and proclaiming very different prices. Against such a background the human picture prevailed—bedding, laughter, food, a communal warmth, and such lovable minutiae as the little ladder in the men's wash-place for the use of the shortest little boy, and the case of the pregnant woman who refused until the very last moment the doctor's orders to go up to hospital—because she wanted to have her baby in the familiar tube and to call it 'Aldwych'.

Most of the shelterers in the Aldwych tube and in other large shelters were not Westminster residents—they came from the East End and from south of the river. They were attracted by Westminster's heavy buildings and the concentration of deep tubes. The inflow was regular. At first there were queues outside shelters, pathetic and impassive lines of mostly women and children standing with their bundles of bedding in any weather, in the rain, in the black frosts. They stood thus from midday till the late afternoon when shelters were reopened by their marshals. Eventually this situation, aggravating above the bombing itself, was regularized and tickets were issued for each shelter and each bunk. People became so used to their particular place in the shelters that, as with warden's posts and other stations of the Blitz, small personal belongings were brought and there developed an atmosphere much on contemporary lips—'home from home'. Different classes, for all the common ground of war, tended to segregate. Thus in one large shelter in the Park Lane district a number of *wealthy* east-enders gathered, bringing with them even wardrobes and trunks. Then there was the taxi-drivers' shelter in Leicester Square. There was another shelter that received its major complement from the blacked-out ranks of the demi-mondaine. Such segregations were not the rule—but there was this tendency. It was the same tendency that was to be found in all the mixed ranks of the war services; while people greeted each other and thought of each other on a common and more human level, nevertheless the fact that certain groups had certain interests-in-common—a practical impulse that has too often been presumed as snobbery—tended to divide again the closed ranks. And the most intense instance of this, at the very end of the scale, was the shelter that became known as the Hungerford Club.

When bombs first fell, vagrants from the embankment and the steps of the Ritz decided for once to enter the community—and took shelter. Invariably in a verminous condition, they took their places in the public shelters and disposed generously of their wealth upon their neighbours. Shelter marshals were faced with a difficult problem. They tried to induce the verminous into isolation bays within the shelters—not always with success. However, a group of some fifty vagrants took possession of one of the little-used arch shelters in Hungerford Lane underneath Charing Cross Station. This was Arch 173. As time continued, it accumulated a residue of filth. The vagrants lit seven or eight open fires, and looking into the arch at night, a tall dark-ceilinged cavernous place, Dickensian and in the same gloomy Hungerford Lane where Dickens himself spent his boyhood of the blacking factory—one saw only haunches and lower torsos squatting round the red fires, for the heads were long lost in a pall of smoke that hung down and filled the tall arch from its ceiling. Macabre, noisome, this scene had to be shifted: and the idea was conceived of transforming another of the arches into a combined air-raid shelter, cleansing station and welfare centre. The City installed baths, bunks, a canteen and a first aid post. The Anglican Pacifist Fellowship undertook to staff the new specialized shelter, felicitously and cleverly called 'The Hungerford Club'. It was opened on 26th February 1941.

The opening night's population came mostly from the infamous Arch 173, though others from other shelters arrived later. The first task of the staff was always the riddance of vermin. Of the four thousand five hundred destitute people who passed through the club, very few were not infested. The record was won by a man upon whose clothing 15,000 lice were counted. Innocently, he helped medical research into the problems of combating lice and louse-carried diseases such as typhus, for all lice gathered at the Hungerford Club were transported to various research laboratories, such as that of the School of Hygiene and Tropical Medicine. It is evidence of the success of the staff in cleansing the inmates of the club that eventually the supply of lice became so low that these Pacifists decided to breed lice on themselves to ensure the regular supply asked for by research workers.

The interior of the club premises became like many other air-raid shelters—bunks (a room for men, and a room for women) a canteen and tea-urn, a wireless-set and a bare swept-up look alternating with the crowded evening *scena* of bedclothes and people. The club always retained some of its ragged appearance—there was washing hanging about, and the very height of the arch lent a cavernous gloom to the place. Yet on floor level there was a deal of content, as the old people gathered round the fire and as sometimes there were entertainments and games, dancing and film shows. Political arguments thrived in the throats of Hyde Park orators, military tactics were torn to contemptible shreds by veterans of previous wars.

On an average some eighty people spent the night and part of the day in this place that became their only home. None were admitted below the age of thirty; that was one of the only rules of entry. The doors were open to anyone, special blue return tickets were issued, above all, those who became members were given no hint of patronage, every attempt was made to revive their self-respect and a respect for others. Their destitution is in many cases due not so much to an insoluble poverty as to a grudge against life and society, a poisonous guilt or a memory of ill-treatment flowered into obsession. Ignorance, fear and prejudice had to be removed with patience and understanding, rather than by lectures and moral discipline. There were physical obsessions, too—some of the members of the club were methylated spirit drinkers, one was a drug addict.

With little exception, the club showed a record of success. Though many members were incurable vagrants, even to these a new interest in life was given. And many others were resuscitated altogether. Others who were only temporarily destitute were found jobs and given a fresh start. One among many letters received deserves quoting.[1] Here

[1] For obvious reasons the name and address are excluded.

are the first lines of this letter, an essay of discovered responsibility:

'Thank you for assisting me in time of need, and I am fixed up O.K. now, and please find enclosed 10s. towards your organization.'

Of the main body of ordinary shelters, much has already been said. In the West End and other parts, where the buildings were large and stable, basements were cleared and towards the end of 1940 proper water closets were installed. Steel bunks took the place of the benches that were expected from the first to be a temporary comfort during short raids. In the question of bunks, Westminster was one of the first among the boroughs to purchase a quantity—some 12,000 before the Government distributed its general issue. These were placed in the deep tube stations, in basements and also in trench and surface shelters.

Thus the comfort grew. First aid was, of course, a first consideration, and in many of the larger shelters first aid posts were staffed by the Red Cross and St. John's. Small libraries were formed, entertainments were organized, even a laundry service was arranged—all so that sheltering should be in every way a relief and a comfort, rather than an imposition added to those already burdening the already strained and weary people who carried on the business of the town and the effort of war production. A good night's sleep, in some comfort, was essential. As far as possible it was provided.

CHAPTER III

AFTER THE RAID

Besides the immediate succour of the wounded and the quenching of fire, it was the City's instant need to see that its running order should be resumed as soon as possible. Energy had to be restored, the broken wheels patched and given oil. First, there was the immediate life of the people to be considered—and most pressing the need of those who overnight had lost their homes and their possessions and the background of their life. Secondly, the metropolitan machinery had to be repaired—the highway made passable, broken water-mains mended, the affairs of sewage and power put in order so that the City might again live. However often the foot disturbed the anthill, however high the piles of debris rose and the intricate works were crushed, automatically the forces of rehabilitation went into action.

REST CENTRES

When people were evacuated from their houses, perhaps in the small hours of the morning, by bombs exploded or unexploded, they were sent by a warden to what was called a Rest Centre. Of these, there were normally five in Westminster. They were run by the L.C.C. Their function was to give immediate shelter and rest for the remainder of the night to those rendered homeless, to give them as much comfort as could be possible, to provide them with a transit camp where particulars of their condition might be registered and arrangements made for their later and more permanent billeting. In the morning after a raid, Westminster officials would visit the Rest Centres and begin necessary arrangements for billeting or rehousing, and for the provision of immediate necessities—money and ration cards and clothes.

Rest Centres in Westminster were housed in several school buildings situated at strategic points. As in most phases of A.R.P. development, conditions began at a primitive level—providing in the first days of the Blitz the absolute necessities of a roof and sleep and sandwiches and a hot drink. But in the course of time comfort was organized down to the last detail, from full-strength hot meals to bird-seed for bombed-out budgerigars, from bunks and bedding to a special intelligence liaison with the Armed Forces so that men abroad might be flown back immediately on compassionate leave.

When the searchlights threw down their starlight and the guns flashed, it was a drab school gate that welcomed the weary and shocked evacuated, those whose houses had been blasted and bombed and who carried not even a bundle with them, not a purse, who often wore no more than a nightgown with somebody's coat thrown over it; together with the bombed came men and women and children ordered out of their houses by the threat of a time-bomb, people who had hurriedly assembled their most intimate necessities, plumped them in a suitcase or bundled them in a sheet and then had made their way to the school gates. Drab gates, but not at times like that—for here was promised rest and relief from the suddenly somersaulted square yards of their home, here was attention and the care of an organization; however people may have reasoned that the authorities could in the last resort offer little more safety than could their own homes, at such moments of hopelessness and helplessness there was an instinct to rely on some protection, some organized protective body. This the Rest Centres provided.

When, towards the end of the year, the process of reception became fully reorganized, the comfort of the homeless was looked after in the greatest detail—there were provided good hot meals, improvised bathrooms with hot water, medical rooms, and even special accommodation for pets with kennels, bromides, special foods. But despite these attempts to make life for the homeless as pleasant as possible, it was vital also to keep them moving. Some stayed a few nights, others a few weeks—according to their means and personality. However, no one knew what inundation of newly stricken people might be expected on the following night, and thus the next step was for the Westminster housing officer to accommodate the temporary residents quickly in the more permanent Westminster hostels, or with householders providing billeting space. Previously the City had provided emergency ration cards and money (sometimes after a heavy raid as much as £10,000–£15,000 was carried by the visiting officer: this did not come as from the Public Assistance Board, it was instead a pure gift, the right of the people). Now a further stage in their rehabilitation had to be effected: rehousing.

AFTER THE RAID

REHOUSING

Of people dishoused by enemy action, 5,366 were temporarily accommodated in rest centres, 3,754 were rehoused in requisitioned houses and hostels, and 3,456 were billeted. Billeting and rehousing was in the hands of the Rehousing Officer, who maintained in his headquarters various departments dealing with all requirements of the homeless, i.e. Information, Assistance Board, Welfare (Lord Mayor's Fund), Removal and Storage of Furniture, First Aid Repairs to Houses, Clothing (issuing store), the Citizens' Advice Bureau, and representatives of the Food Office and National Registration Office. Not only the immediately bombed homeless, but also evacuees and refugees came within the control of this officer. Thus he was concerned as early as May 1940 with the billeting of Belgian refugees and in July 1940 with the arrival of a few evacuated persons from the English coastal areas.

During the Blitz his real work began, and the number of people in billets and in Westminster hostels rose to its highest peak in January 1941—when 1,800 persons were accommodated at one time. Thereafter a decline was shown, checked by the great raids of April and May 1941, until the end of the first period of bombing. Though the department was for periods most active, and though the inquiry office dealt with never less than 100 calls a day, even during the Lull period, nevertheless the heaviest duty for which the department was prepared never practically arose. This was a scheme prepared in case of German invasion or of concentrated bombardment of the coastal areas in time of an allied departure for the Atlantic Wall—the accommodation of evacuees from the coast to the amount of 9,000, who had all to be received within four days. To deal with this remarkable influx, a most detailed plan was arranged and seven large reception areas scheduled; but the need never arose.

The main hostels of the Blitz period were improvised in empty mansions in Belgravia and Mayfair. Requisitioned and furnished by the City, they were staffed with housekeepers and cleaners under the direction of the Women's Voluntary Service. The number of hostels fluctuated. At one time 67 were prepared, and at another—after some had been seriously damaged by bombing—54 were on the rota. In addition to these small hostels, there was the central hostel, capable of holding 300 persons, situated in the large block of Park Lane flats called Gloucester House. Here also were the offices of the Women's Voluntary Service, the large British Restaurant and underneath garage accommodation for mobile canteens. Apart from these arrangements, many of the homeless were billeted in private houses, and often stayed on afterwards as ordinary paying guests outside the auspices of the Council. Several unfurnished flats were also taken over by the Council, for families wishing to set up their own homes again.

Community living proved much more popular than had been expected. Families who might have been thought anxious only to set up their own homes again chose to remain in the hostels. This appeared to be due largely to wartime difficulties of housekeeping and catering; and when these troubles were eased housewives could, of course, go out to a daily job. However, hostels were never intended as permanent residences; though they were more permanent than rest centres, they were intended for a convalescent period while at their leisure people might pick up again the strands of life and find their new homes. The large number who wished to make the hostel permanent seems to evidence their success. However, living was not free—although on a full board basis it was undoubtedly inexpensive. Rent for a family of four amounted to 12s., with board at 10s. a head and a charge of some 4s. for fuel and light. It was possible to reduce even these charges.

Specialized hostels were also provided. A house in Eaton Square was taken for aged and slightly infirm people. The proportion of the aged in relation to the total population of Westminster was high. It was generally most difficult to persuade them to leave London. In spite of all danger they preferred to stay at home, among familiar things, with their memories. When they were bombed, then special arrangements had to be made for their comfort, and in the house at Eaton Square it was made possible for them to achieve at least a shadow of their old home-life in or near to the district that they knew as theirs. Other special hostels included two to cater for the special needs of the Jewish faith; here for instance, only kosher food was cooked.

Early in 1940 the Council decided to purchase furniture in anticipation of the needs of those whose homes might be broken. This furniture, with that supplied by the Government and much that was received by way of gift, was used to furnish the hostels; the surplus was stored against future need in the Council's furniture store.

The Rehousing Officer was, in fact, the City Valuer. So that allied to these housing problems, there accumulated for this department throughout the war an unusual weight of valuation work, in abnormal conditions, in revision of all the old premises of valuation, with rates fluctuating according to damage and to the vagaries of business in wartime. This proved a considerable work, but cannot be detailed here, where our concern is with the more immediate post-raid problems and services.

MORTUARIES

Second to the care of living was the care of the dead. Before the war, when casualties on a very large scale were expected, plans were laid for four air-raid mortuaries in different parts of the City. Special card-board coffins were manufactured and stacked in their thousands, canvas shrouds were designed that would serve both the purpose of shroud and coffin. Fortunately none of these mass methods of reception became necessary. Only one wartime mortuary was operated, in addition to the City's peacetime institution.

Though demands of space were adequate, other difficulties arose. For instance, a large number of bodies were sometimes recovered at dawn. Many were mutilated, all covered with dust. These had all to be identified. Identification required a special technique, which could only be learnt through experience. This involved the putting together of factual evidence deduced from the body, from its clothes and posses-sions, and later from the interview with relatives who had come to look for their missing. In a place such as Westminster, the problem proved more difficult than that of a purely residential district. Many who were killed had come to London perhaps only for the night, or for a short time—and on their person no clue might be found to the place where they lived. In this regard, the Council kept all clothes and possessions of the dead—and in one case a person killed was identified as long as three years later, following new inquiries and the production of one garment.

The interviewing of relatives and friends took place in offices attached to the mortuary. These interviews needed, as must be imagined, tactful and sympathetic understanding—they were moments of grief, and how-ever accustomed the mortuary staff became to the physical handling of the dead, they never grew hardened to these interviews that demon-strated the real extent of human suffering. And here mention must be made that, although the regular mortuary staff was augmented by specially recruited men, there were times when a larger staff became necessary. Procedure at the mortuary is of necessity slow and pains-taking, and yet speed is essential. So that on many of the mornings after the heavier raids, many of the staff of the Public Health Department volunteered to help—not only in clerical capacities but in all the other unattractive physical duties. Any unpleasant duty was undertaken by men totally unused to the sight of the dead; and this, it must be remembered, took place in the cold hours of day after the raid, not in the heat of the bombardment itself. It is notable that after several heavy Saturday raids members of the staff arrived unasked on Sunday morning to bear a hand at the mortuary.

The intimacies of so cruel a subject need not be investigated here. Briefly, it may be said that the whole question of dealing with the dead was conducted with accurate and decorous care. Officers were appointed to trace relatives. There was immediate liaison with the police. The Town Clerk was empowered specially to register death, without the services of a doctor or registrar. There were special arrangements made for interment in the City's burial ground at Hanwell. A part of this cemetery had been put aside by the City, and here every attempt was made to give a right respect to the dead, and to avoid what some citizens feared—the idea of a 'common burial'. Priests of specific denominations officiated, there were coaches supplied for the mourners, the coffins were overlaid with a Union Jack. These attentions were provided free of any charge.

The only occasion of a communal civic burial was that following the disaster at Rogers House. Then a memorial service was held at St. Stephen's Church, Rochester Row, conducted by the Canon of Westminster and the Rector of St. John's. The Mayor and members of the Council and Civil Defence services were present in mourning for those twenty-one of the City's dead.

SALVAGE OF EFFECTS

It was found in the course of bombing that one of the most valuable services that could be rendered to the bombed was the recovery of their personal effects: afterwards, of their furniture and heavier possessions —but at the time of disaster, those personal necessities and small objects of sentimental value that were their relation with the old life. For this, a Personal Effects Department was instituted; and a staff employed to search the debris. When all seemed lost, when the house they had lived in stood so empty and shattered, dead, or merely a mound of rubble with no character left whatsoever . . . it was then to those standing hopelessly, blankly in the street, that a great joy could be brought by the recovery from the ruins of some living possession, some suggestion that life was not after all over—a wedding dress, photographs or letters, a worthless brass candlestick, a family Bible.

Much was taken back to the Council's Depot, where there accumulated an endless miscellany of every kind of object, from dental instruments to the regalia of Orders, from Victorian underwear to modern hardware, from theatrical dresses to typewriters and bills and diaries. Quantities of cutlery were found scattered through the debris, and it was a colossal task to collect these again into their right sets, house by house, flat by flat. Large sums of money were found—for in Soho, for instance, many of the foreign residents had never trusted their savings to a bank, thinking the currency might perhaps depreciate, and so kept all their money in their homes, in boxes, in bags. Some carried large sums about with them, and amounts upwards to £500 were found in shopping-bags or carefully wrapped in a linen 'pocket' at the bottom of a hold-all. Beside the money there would lie heavy old-fashioned jewellery, watches, gipsy-rings, gold Alberts and lockets.

The spectacle of these close possessions, each speaking of one person's life or of a way of life, brings one to similarly close quarters with the human distress of bombardment in a city; closer quarters perhaps in the sight of such loved trifles and intimacies than in the sight of blood itself; closer even than the destruction of whole houses. In this province further tragedies occurred: at one incident a woman inquired for a box which contained some £80 in notes, and which she had placed between the wall and a hot-water tank for safety. It was nearly five months before it was found. Finally, when the box was opened the money lay silted at the bottom in fine shreds, hardly recognizable. Rats or mice had been at it. The woman was very naturally distressed, and her only course was to take the box along to her bank for assessment. For at banks, great patience was exercised in piecing together such fragments and ascertaining if possible any serial numbers. If these could be established, the claimant was allowed the value of the note represented. There were many cases of this kind.

The Personal Effects Officer came across instances of fortitude such as that of the woman whose home had been wrecked by blast and who came up to the officer as soon as he arrived, saying: 'Can I have my sewing machine, which has just been got out, once I get that I can soon earn money to buy the other things that's gone.'

And he had to deal with such strange conferences as that held with a small girl of ten who had been brought by a family of Italians to act as their interpreter. It was pathetically indicative of the upset world to watch then the way this little girl managed with a firm hand her mother, aunts and grandmother, asking and giving intelligent questions and answers, taking the whole family in stern hand.

There were also to be considered those personal effects that were found on the dead. The department dealing with these was separate, and run in conjunction with the mortuary. Again large sums of money were found, £300 on one man, much jewellery on another; and there were hundreds of pounds of jewellery worn by some of the women dead. One curious common feature among these possessions was the incidence of the travelling saint—an astounding number of effigies of St. Christopher were found worn round the neck. Less reverent was the discovery of a jemmy strapped to the leg of one man; and of forty ignition keys found in the pocket of another. And on one occasion an identity card was found which the police took to its inscribed address. At the door they told their story, how Mr. X had been killed. The man who had opened the door only smiled. 'Thanks', he said, 'for telling me . . . I'm Mr. X.' The identity card had been stolen.

Added to the collection of personal effects came the job of salvaging stocks in shops. This was not properly a duty of the Council, but as much help as possible was given to local traders. At a West End wine merchants', for instance, some dozens of bottles of champagne were retrieved several days after the incident. After the bombing of a military tailors', 1,500 garments were washed and dried at the Council's baths, together with 750 uniforms and 385 rolls of material. These figures are mentioned to show that this, though only a small part of the general service of rehabilitation and economy, played no insignificant part.

The general salvage of furniture had to be considered. This too was undertaken by the Council—with help at such times as the flying-bomb period from outside forces like the National Fire Service. Salvage of furniture did not necessarily mean a straight removal. Often pieces had to be recovered from houses considered unsafe, which were not indeed likely to fall, but parts of which might nevertheless have collapsed, and particularly in the event of a further explosion nearby. However, in the main, it was a job of freeing furniture from the water and dust-soaked ruins and of transporting it to the Council's various improvised furniture stores. In all, 2,074 lots were removed from bombed sites.

In time of war, when the national economy is watched with care and every effort made to increase the productive effort, salvage of such material as bricks and hardcore for building becomes of importance. Westminster salvaged many thousands of pounds' worth from the mess of ruin—some 1,230,000 bricks, 76,000 tons of hardcore, 4,400 tons of iron and steel, 560 tons of lead and other metal.

Vital also was the need not only to salvage as much food as possible, but also to condemn contaminated food that might endanger the public health. Council inspectors visited food shops in the morning after a raid, estimated the damage, removed polluted goods in a specially equipped van. Much loose commodities such as flour and sugar would be sent back for refining—even sugar filled with glass could be made fit for use again. Many tins were needled with fine punctures of glass, the sharp slivers then nesting unseen inside among the contents; much care had to be exercised to be sure that these were not put on sale again. Glass was the main danger; it could be powdered and mixed with tea, for instance, in such a way that its presence was invisible until fingers dipped in the tea showed a minute rash of cuts. On one occasion a window-full of peaches were made possibly lethal with glass splinters absorbed. Heat from fires affected canned goods, the inside lacquer permeating the food with metallic poison. Altogether 462 tons of food were removed by these sanitary inspectors; 241 tons were passed as fit for human consumption and 86 tons of various commodities—such as condensed milk—relegated to animal feeding.

Finally, when all that could be done was done with the retrievable necessities of life, there was the ultimate form of salvage—the salvage of waste material for reconversion. After the first year of war, when imports into these islands were substantially lowered, every effort had to be made to increment for munitional purposes stocks of materials like paper and rubber.

A Nation Salvage drive was propagated. Westminster held the national record for the highest salvage yielded per thousand population. Though this perhaps did not take into account the use of material by the large daily visiting population, it attests nevertheless to the effort that was made to gather up what was in fact yielded. Nearly 3,000 tons of iron were provided for re-use in iron and steel works from an up-rooting of railings. One of the largest items became waste paper, of which 13,113 tons were collected.

The Council installed a plant for the sterilization and processing of kitchen waste. This had a capacity of 250 tons a week, and from it there exuded the immense cylindrical sausage of processed food that was in total sufficient to feed 31,000 pigs from birth to maturity. Prior to this installation, enough had been sold to farmers to feed another odd 2,000 pigs. Of the raw tonnage of this waste, 14,000 tons were collected in Westminster and 21,000 tons delivered to the plant by adjoining boroughs.

CLEARANCE OF DEBRIS

It was first imagined that glass splinters scattered over the streets would prevent vehicles from driving through the blast area of a bomb. But it happened differently—tyres withstood the glass well. Though such instant dangers were averted, the glass itself had to go, the bricks, too, and timber and girders thrown across the street. Later the building sites themselves had to be cleared of their insanitary and depressing rubble. So the Council organized its transport to clear the streets; after heavy raids, when the situation saturated available lorries, then contractors' vehicles were hired. Various departments took their share, and many hundreds of men were at work on the streets and at sites on the day after a raid and for weeks following. The L.C.C. put into operation a War Debris Survey scheme and removed much of the heavier debris; the Heavy Rescue Service were employed in demolition, as were also the Pioneer Corps. Of a total debris collection of 332,340 tons, 119,265 tons were barged away on the Thames from the Council's Depot south of Victoria. In this instance, there was at times concern at the danger of the Thames being made impassable by plane-laid mines; at times barges were held up; there was a fear that garbage would accumulate; but throughout the whole war this danger never became excessive. Not many mines were dropped, or drifted up-river; and, in any case, the Navy swept the water as far north as Teddington at dawn after every night-raid.

The streets after a raid always looked dusty, disagreeable, tattered, depressive. The incidence of broken houses and shattered shops had its effect on the people. It was a reminder of war, and thus perhaps salutary; but a most unsavoury reminder, not sharp in its impact but dulling and of a damping monotony. It was thus that apart from all material reasons these clearers of debris did useful work in cleaning up the appearance of the battered town, heartening the streets again, shipping off the damage and revealing thus in clear and empty spaces much light and less destruction than would otherwise have appeared, mouldering, among rows of houses that seemed instead to straighten themselves out into life again.

AIDS TO MOVEMENT OF TRAFFIC

The blackout was constantly in the minds of Londoners throughout the war; in their minds, on their shins, in their noses bruised on lamp-posts and sometimes in their waking moments in the casualty ward. It never failed to provide meat for the humorous papers, it never failed to aggravate the discomfort of the times. However, as much was done as possible to mitigate its ubiquitous shadow. Westminster's problem proved acute, for here vast crowds accumulated and at least the military and other official traffic was constant. An absolute blackout of street lighting was thought inadvisable.

At the beginning of the war lights were ruthlessly cut off. But in December 1939 the Government approved a scheme for restricted— very restricted lighting. 'Star-lighting' became the order of the night, a dusty bluish glow that with its pinpoints at least marked the direction of the street and provided occasional landmarks. By a special effort, streets within a radius of half a mile of Piccadilly Circus were fitted with this lighting by Christmas of 1939. Thereafter the moon was the only further mitigation; otherwise pedestrians and motorists used to mark their way mostly by the inky skyline of the street against the usually lighter darkness of the sky. Not until November 1944, when the era of bombing had entered its pilotless phase, was there a partial relaxation of 'starlight'. Then 'moon' lighting began, and the streets became more comfortable.

When streets were closed by bombing additional oil-lamps were distributed; on one night in November 1940, 2,540 oil-lamps were put into use. More permanent oil-lamps were used for such military obstructions as defence posts and barbed-wire barriers. Refuges, islands, and other permanent growths were illuminated by 'St. Andrew's Cross' lights. 2,147 masks, with small apertures in the form of a cross, were fitted to traffic signals. White traffic lines became a feature of the town; trees, pillar-boxes, kerbs and other traps for darkened feet were painted white. 28 miles of roads received white lines, 2,860 other places were painted white. 7,400 gallons of white paint were used.

OTHER SERVICES

Much of the work described in the above passages cannot make dramatic reading. But to those who undertook it the dramatic significance was apparent, their work took them up against the residue of bombing while it was still hot, they in their offices or in the streets worked on through raids without the palliative of vigorous action. They often worked days and nights and Saturdays and Sundays. They had, in any case, less leave than the uniformed Civil Defence Services: and with the more senior officers the burden was even increased. During lull periods, their work knew little respite, and in addition the ordinary welfare of the city had still to be administered: public health had to be watched, ordinary repairs effected.

There is a tendency to consider Civil Defence in terms of nurses, firemen, rescue workers, and other active personnel. But the ordinary staff of the Council and their officers played a long, arduous, un-bemedalled and willing part. All the paraphernalia of planning and re-organization, of pay and maintenance, of equipment and welfare, of construction and of defeating at every turn the accumulating destruc-tion—these were ingredients of hard, ceaseless work: apart from fire-watching and the Home Guard parades which invaded further what leisure might be left: apart from the maintenance of a home in those times of distress: apart, often, from being blasted out or bombed. These men, many of them what the man-in-the-hole-in-the-street derisively dismisses as a 'penpusher', accepted these added strains, long abnormal hours, and hard extra work with willing patience; not for a few months, but throughout the war, and in some instances for several years before the war.

Added to their ranks, in various degrees of manual and mental duty, were other officers and men applied to departments not hitherto men-tioned. The Food Office, administered by the Town Clerk, burdened exceptionally in Westminster by the large number of hotels and res-taurants and the constant change of population. Then there was the City Comptroller's office dealing with intricate financial stresses, with new and involved disbursements on a huge scale and acting also as the Fuel Office. The City Engineer's department that organized first aid repairs to houses, so that in a steadily dilapidating neighbourhood people might still find a roof above their heads and the draught of their glassless windows covered. The Catering offices, where emergency and other food had to be organized. The Stores, where all A.R.P. equipment was housed. The garages where the Council maintained its heavily increased wartime fleet of cars and heavy vehicles. And many others, whose offices cannot be detailed here—since this account is by nature impressionist and not of volume large enough to record all the facets of so vast an organization. Add only a word for those outside the Council offices who helped the City keep its breath and get its daily bread—many such as the Covent Garden marketeers who operated throughout the war and who in the worst winters went to their work at the height of the dark early morning raid.

Mention in some detail, however, must be made of the interesting and complex difficulties faced by the utility companies—of electricity works, gas repairs, telephone maintenance and the vital flow of the Water Board—together with the City Engineer's defence of the sewers, his rebuilding of the roads, and his general liaison of all these services that kept the City in essential running order.

In the first place such references do not come within the heading 'after the raid'. Much repair work and reconnaissance was done beneath the empty gunflash of the night, in mud and flood and fire, with the glassy tinkle of steel shrapnel and the great boom of the bomb's subsidence curtaining the streets. The various utility companies maintained control centres, which were informed of damage by the Westminster Control, and which then sent out into the night cars with reconnaissance engineers, or despatched on foot the nearest resident turncock. These reported the situation and mobile repair squads were ordered out accordingly.

When a bomb tore up a street and its near-surface labyrinth of wires and pipes, the process was threefold: first immediate isolation and choice of some diversionary circuit, then temporary detour work around the crater on the spot, and then for long afterwards, often by day and by night, the long business of repairing the conduits and covering in the roads. At one incident, where a bomb fell in a main road, there could be the repair squads of six undertakings at work—sewerage, electricity, gas, hydraulic power, water and telephone—and in consequence somebody had to decide in the morning, when the squads presentéd themselves, who should go into the hole first. This decision fell upon the representative of the City Engineer. He controlled the hole. He sorted out questions of priority and technical precedence and regulated in his liaison capacity the reconstruction of the road from its pit to its level.

In the main, the process of rebuilding had to start at the bottom and proceed upwards; also, one side of the crater had often to be completed first so that the roadway, if completely blocked, could be reopened to traffic. The first job, then, was for the works department to clear the interior of the crater of debris and most of the clay, gravel and mud that made of those rents in the street such an intractable, chaotic mess. Imagine a whirlpool of earth, water, wire and steel suddenly subsided and set; imagine the task of unravelling a knotted spider of many different strings clammily concealed in a ball of waterous clay. The first job, then, was to clean the site so that at least the damage could be seen. Even then it was not a clear matter of revealing the ends of smashed pipes neatly strataed—for the explosion might have fractured those pipes many yards inwards under the earth, when, of course, further excavations would have to be made.

At the same time the priorities were fixed. Water mains, if there was no alternative valve route, were often most urgent. They were allowed a by-pass temporary main out on to the footway. Then, the

Post Office might have a trunk-line of military importance that needed immediate operation: for this a temporary bridge might be slung or the cables erected on a framework. Down in the pit, at a depth of 18 feet, the lowest conduit was always the sewage culvert: so in the hierarchy of rebuilding this had to come first.

Round the bed for rebuilding, a timber shoring was effected. Above the culvert ran the electricity cables; these, with their system of many diversionary circuits, were not always of great urgency. Above or parallel with these ran the hydraulic power mains—small in diameter but spitting a great pressure. Gas mains, though placed slightly lower, waited—for their iron was heavy, and it would not be safe to risk a subsidence of the newbuilt sides of the bed or of the temporary shoring. So that, after temporary measures had been taken for water, electricity and telephone conduits, the first bricks of the blue-bricked bottom of the new sewage culvert were laid. Then upwards through the hierarchy, until the great gas-pipes were fixed and lastly the permanent new water main and the surface of the road.

All this reconstruction was done during bombing, when additional damage was accumulating elsewhere and further complicating priorities and diversions. On several occasions when the work was finally completed, it was immediately disrupted by another bomb. However, at no time were any of the services brought permanently to a halt. Many temporary gaps occurred in local distribution, but in every case these were repaired before long. At one time, towards the end of the 1st September, it did seem that possibly the accumulation of the breakage of hundreds of different conduits might overcome the speed of repairs. But more labour was recruited, the pioneers were sent in to give their welcome hand, and soon the first period of question was answered. Though severely bombed, the City was never saturated like a town beleaguered with artillery fire or thousand bomber raids. Nevertheless, severe breakdowns were experienced: though they were all put to right.

Each of the utilities—gas, water, electricity, telephones and, in a smaller degree, hydraulic power—had their individual difficulties, though in a general way much of their experience was in common. Thus, they each maintained central control-rooms for the reporting of damage, and from these reconnaissance engineers and repair squads were despatched during the night and over the next days and weeks. The Gas Company, for instance, maintained a control-room for its whole area of 400 square miles in a concrete stronghold built into the side of a Victorian gasholder excavation, itself on the site of the earliest gasworks in the world, the Chartered Gas Light and Coke Company of 1812, a contemporary of the London Portable Gas Company of Clerkenwell which proposed to abolish mains and deliver gas to the householder's door in copper containers. So on the cradle-ground of such early beginnings the gas industry kept watch over its leviathan extension during those more modern nights of war. Similarly the Central London Electricity Company maintained a reinforced concrete citadel, equipped with gas-proof dormitories and guarded by barbed-wire barricades and the inspection of photographic passes; this, too, contained in its roots a charming archaism, for encased deep down among so many contemporary conveniences there primped the telephone receivers of the company's private deep-laid electric telephone system, fragile and antiquated instruments of early telephone days, objects entering already into the sphere of romance—yet still sharply alive and an important link in vital war communications.

From such nerve-centres, then, Westminster's needs were maintained. Each service wrestled with its own intimate problems. The Metropolitan Water Board, for instance, had engaged in vast chlorination works of a most intricate nature. But in addition to the purification of water they had to envisage a state of affairs when all waterflows might themselves be obstructed, and so private wells and borings were earmarked (some forty-six in Westminster) and an overall fleet was formed of as many as one thousand mobile water tankers. The wells themselves would have provided a large surplus above the estimated two gallons a day per head for the population.

From a fire-fighting point of view, new large mains were laid and certain others isolated. From the point of view of the kitchen, the disturbance proved to be very temporary, though indeed startling. When in the Blitz a large main was fractured to the north of Hyde Park, the water gushed down into a broken gas main lying alongside. Water, we have been told, finds its own level. Here its level began in the low-lying marsh country of Pimlico and Westminster-by-the-river. Housewives discovered for themselves with some degree of surprise the stark truth of this elementary law when they turned on the taps of their gas-stoves and remarked—little marvel of home science!—upon the fierce and silvery jet of pure water that projected itself thence up into the air and down upon the kitchen floor.

Water run wild was in other ways a severe trouble among operations on the street. In its insistence upon its own level, it flooded craters and basements, sometimes with fatal results, often complicating the work of rescue, saturating wreckage and holding up the work of repair. Conversely, according to the luck of the game and the bomb, it refused altogether to appear when most needed to serve the hoses of the Fire Service. But in regard to flooding, a popular misconception should be corrected. It was often thought that, because water continued to flow from a main long after the incident, no action had been taken by the turncocks. The truth is that when a main is fractured, the operative valve is likely to be remote, perhaps round the corner, perhaps in another street, from the immediate incident. The turncock had therefore to do his job unseen. Afterwards, he returned home to await further calls. But the water had in any case to continue to flow until the main was empty—so to those working at the incident it often seemed as if no action at all had been taken. To exacerbate this misconception, in dealing with so heavy and forceful a material as water, a single valve (and there are usually more than one involved) on a large trunk main may take several men between half an hour and an hour to shut, slowly, laboriously, for if speeded unwisely the main would break elsewhere.

At the street level of an elaborate wartime organization, of infinite and most watertight preparations against all emergencies, there walked the turncock. The turncock lived near his pipes, and his was the duty of turning out on his turncock's walk whenever trouble arose. He turned out at night, in the thick of it, and in some lonely street located his valve and turned slowly the hydrant with his key. The turncock's walk is by day a leisurely affair; by night he hurried, though when arrived at the job he was forced again to turn slowly, slowly—with around him a crescendo of brightening fire.

That brightening fire might have come from a blazing gas main. And that introduces the most severe problem in Westminster for the Gas authorities, the fracture and fire of the mains. None of the Company's gasholders were situated within the City limits, so that the severe and dangerous destruction of such priority targets cannot concern us here; but disruption of the distributory channels was sometimes widespread. As soon as an incident was reported, valve locaters were sent out. These men often had to enter a building on fire and, beneath water from Fire Service hoses, locate their valve and immunize the gas. They could, according to the layout of the system, isolate buildings and blocks by shutting off their valves; sometimes a main fire might be quenched in this manner, too; whole streets badly knocked could be isolated and in other cases the danger of firespread averted.

The treatment of a gas main fire is interesting. These fires did not jet, but towered hugely like the flame of a giant naphtha flare. They burnt with a strong yellow light, rose often above the surrounding house-tops, and produced a singeing heat usually too fierce to allow the approach of an ordinary fireman. Gas engineers dealt with these fires, while the Fire Service sometimes sprayed them or drenched with water curtains the surrounding buildings. Though asbestos suits were issued to gas engineers for the purpose of approaching the seat of the flame itself and plugging the pipe, they were in fact seldom used. The mess of dirt and rubble often concealing the main break prevented plugging, so a system was used of 'bagging' the pipe farther along. Incisions were made in the road with compressor drills, on each side of the break, and holes were cut in the main—which previously had been isolated. Into these holes were inserted long-necked bladders of canvas-covered rubber. Air was pumped through, the bladders swelled—and the pipes were gagged. Later the true work of repairing the broken pipe was pursued by heavy repair gangs.

The Gas Company's greatest trouble was with water—allusion to which has already been made. Sometimes it took as long as a fortnight to pump out water strayed from a broken water main. It became of prime importance to keep the pipes absolutely dry—even in peacetime one of the main problems of gas distribution had been to prevent condensation in the pipes.

As with other utilities, gas had its importance in maintaining morale. It was vital to get cookers going. It was important, too, that the 'gas man' made his usual round of the morning streets, as if there had been no blitz, providing a welcome link with an old life that might, in the broken streets, have seemed to have disappeared for ever.

A place like Westminster naturally contains many telephone exchanges. From a Civil Defence view this was of first importance, for, with several alternate lines messages could be thus more easily re-routed when first communications were broken. A high concentration of private switchboards (at various ministries, offices, etc.) and of priority lines, complicated the system in the Westminster area: though to cover this close network there was available a staff of as many as one thousand telephone engineers.

The central control was located in the Gerrard Street Exchange. Such was the system of diverting lines that never at any time during the war did there occur a complete breakdown, no place ever being isolated from a telephone at any one time by more than one quarter of a mile. However, greater danger than the bombs lay in a 'flood' of calls. This was realized in full degree when Mr. Chamberlain returned from Munich and made his speech in the House: after the announcement the system was temporarily swamped. So that all through the war there was operated a technique, not generally known to the public, of dousing on a large scale all originating calls from private non-priority telephones. This was never imposed for long—but it was, in fact, vitally necessary. Taking into account the huge population and the compounding of the news impulse during a raid, it becomes plain that even so vast a system as was laid in Westminster could not stand the racket. Herein also lies the answer to the question: 'Why were wardens encouraged to run to their posts with reports, rather than telephone?'

Repair squads attended breaks in the various lines during raids. They continued their slow work of locating and twisting together the thousands of copper wires under bombardment, throughout those long nights squatting in their manholes with often only a sheet of tarpaulin over their heads. Enclosed in the lead sheath of a telephone cable there might be as many as 2,800 wires torn: each of these had to be located and reconnected, down in that pit, by a small light—slow and calm work beneath the tornado overhead. Each wire possessed a subscriber and an exchange; each of these had to be located. And sometimes there occurred multiple breaks, in places where the subscribers' lines merged into junction cables nearing the exchanges. In one case, for instance, forty-two cables altogether were broken in the Piccadilly crater opposite St. James's Church; this particular crater illustrates some of the contributory troubles that had to be faced—such as a blocked up sewer that suddenly broke open and deluged again the torn mass of cables and pipes.

Work at the exchanges themselves continued throughout the heaviest bombing. The voice that spoke to you, say, from the Gerrard Street Exchange came from under a steel helmet. The operators' desks were on the top floor, above lay only a thin roof and then the vast active dome of the night sky. The voice came from a room of masked electric light, quiet burrings and polished wood (in telephone exchanges the floors are of waxed parquet, dust is a great danger to the delicate machinery) and then through the wires it travelled down and past the automatic exchange rooms (rooms full of queer tickings, rooms like libraries of quiet steel books ranged in orderly cases) to the beginnings of the trunk lines, row upon row of subterranean leaden tentacles ranged on racks and all pulling still downwards into the earth.

Much of the secret life behind the telephone wires remains to be told, much for which there is not space here. How, for instance, the basement of the German Embassy had to be watched and the direct route outside examined, in case they had 'borrowed' lines from the War Office; how manhole covers were sealed, not so much to prevent tapping—which is in any case a difficult and obvious business—but to preclude the sabo-teur; how special equipment such as wire-carrying slung bridges were invented to cope with emergency situations; how water could penetrate burst cable, and erode the paper separating wires—so that at times privacy between subscribers was invaded, a danger from the security viewpoint; how cables could be stretched a quarter of a mile away from the bomb and how only the setting up of a Regional Control could de-cide whether an interruption to the trunk-line to Portsmouth had been caused by a bomb in Victoria or another miles away at Merton. These are all part of a fascinating and generally unknown life—and all part of a considerable war achievement that kept London's and West-minster's communications system up to the mark in those chaotic times of nightly severance.

The affairs of the Central London Electricity Company centred in Westminster round its substations. The area contained six of these—each of which supplied as much electricity as an average provincial power station. And there were bred from each of these further installa-tions, the many small transformer units. Thus, although electricity was not such a dangerous material as water and gas, the electric company had not only to fear damage to its distributive cables but also to the complicated switch-gear installed throughout the City.

On occasions this was hit. As has been related, fire destroyed the sub-station in St. Martin's Lane, ruining many tons of equipment. Another bomb fell on a corner of the station in Duke Street, penetrating a cable chamber containing a multiple run of outgoing high voltage cables; there it exploded, damaging 80 per cent of the outgoing cables and buckling the control switchboard. On the same night fifteen trans-former stations in the St. James's district were put out of commission by cable destruction in roadway craters. So that one of the Central London Electricity Company's problems was to replace damaged gear. This the company had foreseen and provided against. Before the war a vast amount of machinery was purchased and laid in as a reserve stock. This foresight, and the previous installation of a system of inter-connecting devices that permitted quick diversionary routes for power between district and district—these kept up the standard of supply throughout the difficult times. However, permanent repair work could not be completed quickly. After the 10th May raid, for instance, the position was not made normal until six months afterwards. During those months, although supplies were maintained, it was, as an official described it, 'like standing on one leg . . . with more than six months before we stood on two legs again'.

Although a torn low-tension wire may remain charged and sharp with shock (it was an old fireman's trick to guide the new recruit's helmet towards a hanging wire and give him a shock to remember) the danger is removed instantly in the case of high tension cables, which are automatically cut dead at source. Thus no great inconvenience was caused to other civil defence activities by the presence of severe electrical dangers—though fires were started under special circumstances. As to the maintenance and repair of cable in the street, much the same problems faced the electric engineer as did the other utilities—an incredibly mixed-up crater, water, sewer atmosphere, escaping gas, and predominantly the mud caking and slithering over the whole distorted puzzle. The electric engineer had to get to work in those same circumstances, locating his trouble by torchlight or by the light of the pyrotechnic night, when perhaps the neighbouring pavements were blue with the fire of underground explosions of gas, when man-hole covers might blow up to meet him.

At the top and at the bottom of the crater of torn conduits lay the constructional responsibilities of the City Engineer—the relaying of sewer culverts and the repair of road surfaces. Besides this, of course, the department had to deal with many other works, including the demolition of dangerous buildings, the construction of blast walls and shelters, the erection of lamp standards (282 of which were damaged). However, here we are dealing with the sewer and the carriage-way. As has been said, the first work on notification of a street incident was the clearance of the crater. Then, since it lay always at the deepest level, the sewer demanded the first repair. It was not as simple as merely laying bricks where bricks had been blown away. Sewage cannot be turned off like water or gas. It continued to silt up behind the block; sometimes tending to force its way back up the gulleys and into private buildings. To avert this danger, pumps were used. At one time, in New Bond Street, for instance, two pumps and one reserve were kept going continuously for about four weeks. Then there was the question of water from a broken main forcing debris from the crater back as far as perhaps one hundred yards up the sewer culvert: such debris had all to be cleared before repair work proper could begin. Serious sewer breakages did not necessarily occur singly—on three occasions as many as eighteen urgent breaks necessitated immediate attention, and a large staff and plant were organized to meet such difficulties; in one month, the month including the heavy raids of April and May 1941, thirty-three sewers demanded attention.

Apart from the rebuilding of these deep brick culverts, there was major work to be done in propping up the sides of the crater to support the new highway to be laid above. In many cases the support previously lent by private vaults and retaining walls could not be reinstated —the owners being unable or unwilling to rebuild. So that special supporting walls had to be constructed to carry the weight of traffic that would later impose itself above. All this, too, in conjunction with works being carried on in the relay of their various strata by the utility companies.

Some idea of the work involved may be gained by mention of one incident—the damage caused by the Piccadilly bomb that fell on the night of 17th April. It fell by Swallow Street, near the vaults of the Piccadilly Hotel, and obliterated under Piccadilly itself all mains, sewers and cables, leaving no part of the carriageway of this important street safe for traffic. First of all, debris from adjacent buildings had to be removed, then a temporary concrete carriageway constructed, partly over the footway and partly over the site of previously demolished premises. Neighbouring vaults were then strengthened, and basements filled with hardcore. This left the field free for work on the various utility conduits. These included: two 18-inch, one 7-inch, two 6-inch and three 4-inch water mains; one 20-inch, one 18-inch, one 12-inch, two 6-inch and two 4-inch gas mains; various electric cables and duct lines; post office telephone cables; one 6-inch hydraulic power main; 105 feet length of 5 ft. 6 in. sewer, a shorter length of smaller sewer, 95 feet of 12-inch pipe sewer and three street gulleys and drains. This laborious work continued without interruption, including week-ends, until, on the 16th September, the street was restored to a proper condition, with no trace left of the damage that had been effected on 17th April . . . five months previously.

However, although there were other serious multiple incidents, they were not always so complicated as on this occasion in Piccadilly. In all the war there were 568 incidents calling for repair to roads, and retaining walls had to be built to support the highway at 296 premises. The main sewers were damaged in 103 places.

THE RIVER

The Thames saw many war-time changes. The White Ensign fluttered against the piles of Westminster's bridges as crab-fat grey auxiliary craft swept for mines; the fireboat *Massey Shaw* came sailing back from Dunkirk; bullet-pocked motor-torpedo boats and gunboats made their way in from action and up-river for servicing; emergency bridges of wood threw their humps across to the southern bank; there came bobbing up with the tide after the dock-raids anything that floated—wax, tallow, bales of esparto grass, charred piles, smashed rudders. These and much else transformed the war-time river prospect in the eyes of anyone watching from the bridges, the embankment, or from Westminster Pier, the centrepoint of the City's reach from The Temple to Chelsea Bridge.

In war-time as in peace, it was the concern of the Port of London Authority to keep the river traffic flowing. As on land, the dropping of bombs and mines was the pre-eminent consideration. At times during the war enemy aircraft sowed magnetic mines as far up-river as Hammersmith. In early days, the Port's tugs swept for mines with only the primitive and dangerous device of a wire drag whose purpose was simply to raise the mine to the surface. But as time went on the naval command, under the Flag Officer, London, organized a daily sweep with naval auxiliary vessels. This sweep was made daily for five years. Owing to the low degree of salinity in the water, the scientific 'Double L' sweep could not be used; but tugs and launches were employed to tow skids. In reserve there were also special minesweepers equipped to deal with the acoustic ground mine.

Such a sweep protected the main channel, but could never comprehend inlets, cuts and other difficult sections of the river. So that when a fully laden oil tanker that had sailed safely from the gulf of Mexico blew up while shifting berth at Thameshaven, it was emphatically brought home that extra measures must be taken to safeguard the side-waters. This stimulated an intensive co-ordination of the mine-watching services on the banks. Fire-spotters, policemen, wardens, Home Guard, watermen, Navy personnel and others combined thereafter nightly in a close watch of the river. Each minewatcher was allotted his post, and from there with a bearing-board he reported degree and distance of any missile seen to fall in or near the water—and from two or three such bearings the naval operations room was able to plot an accurate position. Exercises were held with illuminated balloons released from naval craft. Wrens manned special posts by bridges and overlooking such important buildings as the Houses of Parliament.

There was also the danger of bombs, objects that fell at some 500 miles the hour against a mine's thirty or forty. A volunteer naval cadre was formed to dispose of the more dangerous of these. The work occasioned much digging and sometimes the donning of a diving suit, with then a dark and perilous flounder in three or four feet of slow-oozing river mud.

The Harbour authorities were much concerned also with wrecks and flotsam dangerous to river traffic. Their patrol launches drove up and down river during raids, assessing each reported incident, and getting to work at points of the tideway's trouble. On one particular night, for instance, a barge was blown up opposite Nine Elms on the southern bank. Its wreck could not be found. Then, many days later, an urgent call came from the gunnery training ship, H.M.S. *President*, moored to the Westminster embankment. The P.L.A. patrol launch went out to investigate and discovered the Nine Elms barge squarely underneath the *President*. It had spent days rolling down along the bed of the river and had come to rest under the *President's* keel at high tide. Now, with this foreign body pushing up underneath, the *President* was in danger of buckling. Just as it was growing dark, the P.L.A. tugs got to work with hawsers to drag out the broken hulk. They worked throughout the night, through a heavy raid. Somerset House nearby was hit. An officer present described the water as 'hissing with hot metal'. But the operation was completed successfully. It took six to seven hours. Then, a week later—by much too late a chance—the old barge was blown up by a bomb somewhere else.

In these days the river was navigated in complete darkness. No lights whatever were allowed. It was an ominous and dangerous time on the water, gliding past the dark obstacles, seeing the bridge-piles looming suddenly blacker than the night, straining the eyes towards the jetty that would suddenly appear drifting towards one swiftly as from a fog. With this went the unpredictable peril of the time, as when a barrage balloon was shot down and its wire stretched across the river from St. Thomas. Again, drifting barges and heavy flotsam might complicate the course. Once, though in Westminster's reach such a thing was exceptional, the steering-gear of a 2,000-ton ship lost control and crashed the embankment—by Cleopatra's Needle.

In addition to its patrol system the Port of London Authority formed a River Emergency Service—a war-time auxiliary force, waterborne, of ambulances and general rescue crews. It was formed to render services on the river similar to those organized by the land Civil Defence Forces: to assist bombed ships and their crews, to rescue and evacuate citizens on land cut off by debris or fires, to render first aid and to transport casualties in water-ambulances to liaison points for conveyance to hospital.

Otherwise on the river police launches maintained eight-hour patrols, and added to their peace-time duties of surveillance and rescue the responsibility of helping whenever they could the services of the Port of London Authority. And finally there were the fireboats and fire-floats of the Fire Service, waterborne pumps that supplied from mid-river a flow of water to the emergency water-lines laid down by hose-lorry to the banks, pumps that also at high tide could draw alongside the bank and fought directly any fire by the river or on the bridges.

The men and women who manned these various auxiliary craft were largely recruited from amateurs of the water, of yachting, boating. And they came to be proper watermen. The river breeds its own view of life, a life distinct from the land. On the water, the river becomes London, and away on each side of the broad water the skyline of a hinterland rises and passes like a foreign place. The embankment and its houses, though they might face the river, have a backdoor aspect. There is a special breeze over the water, gusts and gulls. The tide tugs at the buoys, there are pebbles in the mud at high tide. The green waterweed still slimes the dark bridge-piles in whose wet stone surface the dents of bomb fragments still mark their place. The land is approached up steps, up iron ladders. The experience of being bombed on the water is different to that on land. On the water it was relatively safe when high explosive and fire-bombs were dropped—for there could be no debris, no burial. But in the time of the flying-bombs the story was different. A wide blast flew unimpeded on every side as the nose-cap hit the water, and then the river became one of the most dangerous and unprotected places of all London.

RAILWAYS AND TRANSPORT

Both the main terminal stations of Charing Cross and Victoria, their sheds and yards and Thames bridges were disturbed on several occasions by enemy action. Indeed, at times they seemed to have been singled out for special attention. This applied more particularly to the Victoria system, which lies in that area of Pimlico showing a higher concentration of bombs than any other part of the City. Whether the Battersea Power Station lying opposite across the Thames, or some marked bend of the river itself affected the directional run of German aircraft is not properly known. However it was, Victoria became a busy place during raids. It suffered several direct hits on Westminster's first night of high explosive, and thereafter others both on this northerly confluence of lines and farther away on the road south, all incidents naturally having

their effect on operations at the terminus. There were spectacular incidents, such as the heavy unknown weapon dropped on the 21st December, and later such as the Victoria fly-bomb; but more devastating to
the system were certain nights and days of cumulative incidents pro-
ducing together real dangers of disorganization. An example of such
multiple trouble would be the night of 10th May 1941 when five unexploded bombs fell on Victoria Station, temporarily paralysing the
terminus; it is of passing interest in this case to note that a train of
coal trucks was shunted into position to act as a blast wall to protect
certain lines here.

The same applied to Charing Cross, with its experience of the
Hungerford Bridge unexploded parachute mine and the group of
bombs that fell on the morning of the 8th October 1940. There were,
in addition, other occasions of compound trouble for the supervisors
whose earnest it was to keep the trains running.

However, with all this, the lines were never long out of action. They
were disturbed, schedules were altered, trains on many occasions ran
slow and late. But never to any degree that might be called an insoluble
stoppage. Repair gangs worked too swiftly for this. Systems of diversion
were devised to deflect traffic. Fleets of buses had been organized to
carry passengers to alternative stations. Sometimes there were parts of
the line out of commission for as long as forty-eight hours, but then the
nearest alternative lines and the closest alternative stations were advised to travellers, who, with that peculiar enthusiasm to get to work at
any cost to their feet or their strained nerves, managed well with what
could be offered. Any London business or other organization, describing its war experience, will repeat emphatically, and still with some
surprise, how under all circumstances their staffs turned up for duty
on 'the morning after'. No small part of this wonder may be laid at the
door of the railways. Certainly there was a freemasonry on the roads,
among the drivers of private cars and lorries who offered lifts to anyone
who might raise a finger. And certainly there was the shoe-leather and
determination of workers. But the resilience of the railways lay at the
core of this continuance of the City's working life.

Working on a railway is not a light job; the textures are never pretty.
Heavy iron and steel in the yards, acres of glass covering the station,
and the knowledge that the line is perhaps a priority target; the driver's
job carrying his massed weight of train along a track that might at
any moment be breached; the hours spent high in a brittle box of glass
with the signal levers; the hard and heavy work of repair out on the
line . . . and all this in the black-out, with only restricted lighting.

Travelling was shuttered; all blinds were drawn, and in the carriages dismal blue lights threw a sense of shadow over the crowded passengers. The platforms of the termini were darkened and blue-lit. There was much of a military flavour—of all services in groups waiting with their kitbags, or of a solitary soldier bowed down under the weight of his full equipment, a figure armed for action yet symbolic as he sweated across the platforms of all the slow effort and endless tedium, the lonely consecration to khaki smells and gun-oil and boots that make up most of a war. Outside the guns of action flashed, the dark pilots flew high in their fighters. And the people in the stations huddled nearer the nearest doorway as the noise above dived down and that high aerial whistle fluted openly into a hiss of air—in the imagination magnetized to those great glass terminal roofs.

Meanwhile the metropolitan business of London's internal transport proceeded underground through floodgates and platforms packed with shelterers, and above ground in buses that eddied through the disruption on erratic and ever-new routes: but seldom stopping—unless requested by passengers or damage.

The underground railway system encountered many dangers from bombing, of tunnel falls, of possible flood, of direct hits on the line and embankments. Sometimes the amount of work entailed after a raid was enormous. Sometimes major engineering works had to be carried out, large quantities of debris cleared away, damaged rolling stock and bridges repaired, electric power mains restored and damaged cabling repaired. An army of plumbers, glaziers, carpenters, electricians, fitters, were kept fully occupied. The scene after the collapse of tunnelling between Victoria and St. James's Park stations after the 10th May raid was chaotic in extreme; the tunnel was open to the sky, on the line lay a piled confusion of charred beams, torn cables, bricks, sheets of corrugated iron, immense twisted steel girders. Towards such a confusion would be driven the long low open repair trucks—vehicles like goods trucks strange to see in the underground tunnels—and the laborious work of clearance begun. Repair men worked steel-helmeted, often at great personal danger from delayed action bombs nearby, from a further raid, from the possible fall of further debris shaken from above them by the night's reverberation.

The danger of waterflood threatened from the Thames. Certain lines crossing beneath the riverbed were closed each night on receipt of the red warning. Floodgates were installed to isolate sections of tunnelling and platform in danger of breach by water. These gates, electrically operated, weighed as much as six tons and would resist a force of over

800 tons, several times greater than any possible pressure. They could be closed within one minute.

On the bed of Thames above the tunnels themselves, hydrophonic devices were sprawled. These recorded a response to all sounds passing through the water—minute currents being set up that were amplified by valve and transmitted thence by telephone to the Engineer's Headquarters. When eventually the long-range rockets began to fall on London, there was much concern as to the safety of these underground tunnels. No general warning was possible, though a system, secret, had been devised to give a limited warning of their despatch. However, even had a tunnel been breached by one of these deep-penetrating weapons, the damage could have been minimized by operation of the lock-gates.

Both the underground and buses became largely staffed by women. At an average time during the lull period as many as 12,000 women were taking on work formerly the province of men (this is a figure for all London, not for Westminster alone). Of these 7,500 were engaged as bus conductresses, 1,300 as station porters and booking clerks and the rest in various engineering grades. The 'clippies' on the buses became a regular London sight, and they too conducted their buses through raids without drawing up for shelter.

Throughout the war buses worked long hours and on routes exposed to all kinds of bombardment. On some mornings they were diverted miles out of their way by road-block after road-block. Their tall red shapes were seen driving through side-streets that had never seen a bus before; and not only *red* shapes, for towards the end of October 1940, provincial and Scottish buses arrived in London to take the place of those of true London red that had been destroyed or damaged. Thereafter grey buses and green buses, chocolate buses and buses bearing distant place-names such as 'Glasgow' were seen traversing the streets of the West End and elsewhere. At night they kept their course, with windows fabricked against splintering, with blue pinpoint lights inside, with only in the very first weeks the question raised: 'Shall we draw up and shelter?' This did occur, but rarely, for the continuance of normal life and the normal getting from one place to another was more of a concern than the bombs.

In this the public were well served by drivers and conductors, who spent whole days or evenings out on the roads, exposed without a shelter, travelling remorselessly from perhaps a safer environment towards an area known to be enduring particular attention at the time. In this respect, they were superlatively tested in the flying-bomb period, where the most dangerous areas were strongly marked. A driver starting from the relatively secure northern roads of London would, as he passed through the centre, through Westminster in fact, hear growing louder the reports of explosions in southern suburbs like Croydon and Lewisham. He knew he was heading at the speed of his schedule into an area packed with the fall of huge explosives. He drove steadily on.

STREET SCENE

The bus journey introduces us again to street level, to the street scene, and to what Westminster looked like during those years; to what visual changes were forced, and to how people behaved after the Blitz and before the second raids and the period of pilotless attack.

Perhaps the look of things can best be generalized in three ways. First, that the City was battered and though largely still intact, nevertheless pockmarked and shoddy, torn and dulled of its old glitter. In the interim period of the Lull the change was towards a clearing-up of this and a slow refurbishing of general appearances. Secondly, there was the influx of foreign troops, particularly of Americans, and the adaptation of many premises to the needs of extended ministry staffs, of clubs and hostels for troops. There could be felt in all central streets the gearing up of the new offensive effort that had its springboard in England and its administrative stress in Westminster. Thirdly one noticed the spattering of the City with more rationalized air-raid precautionary devices—such as the Fire Service static water tanks and pipelines, and everywhere freshened up notices and inspirational posters making plain the new direction.

The changes themselves changed. At one time after the Blitz there could be seen at the beginning of Kensington Gardens an immense pile of pink rubble, an agglomeration of hundreds of tons of bricks brought there not only from Westminster's bombed sites but from many other boroughs. The pile, which grew to tremendous proportions, rising high against the trees like a palace of oriental coral, undulated its beauty over several acres. Towards its summit could be seen traversing lorry ramps; high up and lost in the immensity a lorry tipped and jerked like a toy machine. There were assorted gardens to this palace—a raised garden of baths and lead pipes, a bosquet of piled doors and window frames. This was an assembly point for rubble that could be again used: so that, as the months went by, and the years, the palace slowly dwindled, disappeared. But it had left its mark on London. It had received rubble from all the sites whose clearance were to give a new character to a cleaner city.

Now in many streets foundations began to appear. Clean foundations, the maps of old kitchens, honeycombs of cellar. And rising above to either side the different coloured wallpapers of rooms that had once occupied the sky. These wallpapers responded to the weather. They were powdered by blast, washed pale by rain, tempered with the light soot: the result—delicate and beautiful colours, colours removed from the drawing-room and now nearer to the subtly weathered washes of a fishing port.

Between these faded colours the empty space gave new perspectives, new angles to the street. In many of the basements the now nationalized Fire Service built the tar and concrete tanks, often holding thousands of gallons of water, that with their new brick walls and their yellow notices were to become a regular feature of the passing street; into these still lakes reflecting on a summer's evening a romance of clean ruin from above, into such enticing lagoons an incredible amount of rubbish was thrown—perambulators and cisterns, dead cats and money, cinders, cages, umbrellas, toys and every conceivable object of disuse. There was then a scare that children would follow the refuse; barbed wire was put up—and torn down. Locks were put on the wooden doors, which were then broken. But the water tanks continued to reflect calmly and continually the nearby ruins and the London sky, the sky speckled with high silver balloons that glinting in the sun were turned magically to fish in the tank. Round about, as in everywhere ruined, grew the rose-bay willow-herb—that straight green weed with the magenta flower whose other name is 'fireweed', for after a forest fire its seed parachutes from nowhere and is the first to grow green on the black acres.

Where the plate glass of shop windows had been smashed, plyboard and papier-mâché facings were erected. These were often centred with a few square feet of glass revealing a miniature window display, while over the boarding around was painted a gay impressionist design of the shop's personality. These indeed lightened the streets, their individuality was welcome to the grey days. Other patches of colour emerged over the paint-faded town; the black and white traffic signals, the yellow and other coloured A.R.P. notices, a wealth of posters appealing to the national effort, flags again and perhaps above all the occurrence of so many new uniforms from all over the world. French sailors with their red pom-poms and striped shirts, Dutch police in black uniforms and grey-silver braid, the dragoon-like mortarboards of Polish officers, the smart grey of nursing units from Canada, the cerise berets and sky-blue trimmings of the new parachute regiments, all the other gaily coloured field-caps of all the other regiments, the scarlet linings of our own nurses' cloaks, the vivid electric blues of Dominion air forces, sandy bush-hats and lion-coloured turbans, the prevalent Royal Air Force blue, a few greenish-tinted Russian uniforms and the suave black and gold of the Chinese Navy. The town moved smartly against its boarded windows and tattered and charred façades. From a liberal viewpoint it is regrettable, but nevertheless true that the imposition of a uniform rather than the free choosing of its own clothes tends to smarten up a crowd.

In the black-out life began again, as soldiers and sailors and airmen on leave took the town. Canadian songs echoed through the dark. The bars were filled and the West End within its shroud took on a new glitter. Though the shops were scarce with whatever was wanted, and though a Tarte de Gaulle of parsnip was sold at the Savoy, nevertheless a brittle good time was had by some and money clinked in all the tills. . . .

Then—the great American invasion. The Americans landed in force. According to their reputation they did things in a big way. In London, they made their headquarters in Mayfair. There had been a popular song 'A Nightingale Sang in Berkeley Square'; now this was parodied 'I heard an Englishman speak in Grosvenor Square'. Americans and American jeeps and other vehicles arrived profusely, American military police with white-painted steel helmets became a sign of the town; these, usually very large men, buckled and fiercely bolstered with arms, came to be called after their white helmets 'Snowdrops'. So the town went gum-chewing, and in many restaurants an American way of life was set. Baseball was played in the parks. Jokes were made about the Yanks. But never before was an invasion so welcome.

Now, as more and more of the military arrived and more and more the ministries expanded, there came to be glimpsed through the windows of many mansions not the brocade curtains and the flowers of more leisurely days, but raw-wood racks and the ends of bunks, brown blankets and files of papers, typewriters and the close-munching faces of a canteen. Clubs were opened, dances were arranged—there was an intent to make the fighting forces at home. And if this seems too bright a picture, it can be set against the London of civilians, the meals of dried egg and turnip pie, the often coal-less firegrates and the queues.

The wish would be too simple a father to the thought if one imagined that Londoners took the Lull with only a cheery smile for each other, with only a helping hand for each smiling neighbour, with a sterling adherence to duty and never a complaint. It would be equally wrong, though, to agree with those who saw nothing but grumbling and rudeness, hard words and bitterness underlying the general façade of give-and-take. It is indeed true that many officials, shop-owners, taxi-drivers, bus conductors and others became overbearing in a way never known before: yet it is equally true that the next one of these would countermand with his great courtesy any convictions formed of a new ubiquitous incivility.

There was, basically, a reaction among artisans and shop attendants to the years of incivility that they themselves had traditionally suffered. Now they were no longer the beggars of trade: and as they held the whip of short supply some tended to express a natural reaction. But not necessarily, not always. Perhaps the only real generalizations that can be made are that during blitzes people generally did smile and co-operate without much grumbling; and that afterwards, in the enervating Lull, having all learned in time of danger to live more deeply, the emotions were freed, and expressed more at either of their limits of anger and generosity—where before such emotions were never expressed, masked so that they were perhaps not even felt. Add to this that they were tired, that the war for them was dragging, that small restrictions were tedious to bear. Add also the stronger social sense, that in its first uncertain mood tends to scourge the asocial rather than follow its true tenet and build the opposite example that will shine and invite.

However, until the first month of 1944 no raids occurred in any strength. But on the nights of 1943 the sirens blew suddenly, their wailing faded, and then there came a huge silence. People listened upwards. The dome of the night-sky expanded, grew more solitary than ever. In the A.R.P. depots and posts scattered everywhere there was a hustle of action, a tuning-up—and then in the silence a slow relaxation. Sometimes a bomber or a fighter scudded across, high. But bombs were dropped only in a limited locality—the greater part of London knew nothing of the isolated tragedy that occurred somewhere in one street drowned in the immensity of streets.

Theatres enjoyed a natural boom. Throughout the war the showing time had been advanced, so that theatres usually played between six o'clock and eight-thirty to nine-thirty o'clock in the evening, with cinemas ending up to ten o'clock. During the Blitz attendance was sometimes meagre, and shows were taken off; others like the Windmill Theatre and the Players' Theatre continued to perform through the worst times without a break. However, in the Lull there came recuperation and new life. The situation relapsed with the new 1944 raids, but by then the general tide of war had changed and the population of the West End saw to it that life should never grow so quiet as during the spirited but futureless days of the Blitz. Entertainment was controlled, night opening in the West End was a matter of permission. However, this was usually granted, although concern was felt in some quarters at the danger of large congregations assembled under bombardment. Westminster, with the greatest complement of theatres and cinemas in England, was extraordinarily fortunate in this respect. There were no major disasters at places of entertainment save the Café de Paris incident.

With London full, hotels and restaurants began to share in the acclerating prosperity. They had had a trying time during the Blitz. During the bombing they made on the whole great attempts to keep open, though in some cases their dining tables were practically empty night after night. They closed earlier, so that their staffs could have the chance to return home, though many slept on the premises. Comfort, appearance, polish are part of the stock-in-trade of the restaurateur, so that blast and darkened windows and other drab intrusions became a serious affliction. Beneath the façade lay the perennial troubles of finding the food to cook—and sometimes the fuel to cook it with: for with temporary failures of power, and sometimes late deliveries of coal, meals in the largest restaurants had to be cooked on spirit stoves and electric fires. Hotels had come to be a necessary national service with so many foreign visitors, with so many on leave, and with many others left without a home. Staffs were depleted, and worked under the most difficult conditions, but they did much to keep the normalcy of life alive, as much in the hard day-to-day round as in cases of peculiar loyalty, as that of one employee who, after his home had been bombed, travelled the next morning across London in his wife's high-heeled shoes so that he could clock in on time at Grosvenor House.

But after the bombing came the Lull, the flowering again of a more complete life, and in their great number the Americans. Out in the streets the debris was cleared. Glass began to go back in some of the more devil-may-care shop windows. In October 1942 General Montgomery attacked at El Alamein. In November the Russians turned the tide at Stalingrad. Then the trumpet time of 1943, year of success. In London there was no talk but it included the Second Front or no Second Front. In Berlin there was a bleating of more and more secret weapons. Across the London skies poured the unending fleets of heavy bombers travelling east and south. Meanwhile, the Civil Defence services, depleted of personnel by the accelerated call-up and of prestige by a public amnesia, were given more and more exercises, equipment and technical training. Which, all things considered, was not to be such a bad thing.

PART THREE

THE LITTLE BLITZ—THE PILOTLESS BLITZ

THE LITTLE BLITZ
THE PILOTLESS BLITZ

The refraction of strange light and strange textures made of that light play on the memory of a bombed street as strongly as the smell, as strongly as the remembered emotion of the moment. Most of the flash and lustre was artificial, and for that reason permutated into many freakish effects—the searchlights above turning to turquoise in the fireglow, the faces yellow in the gaslight, the perpetual sunset coppered and orange above any black roofscape. But broadly at an incident there seemed to be two most regular and most penetrating effects—one of the bombed house cold and away from all firelight, and the other warm and garish in the pantomime light of the fire.

The first, the cold scene, would be lit by the light of the moon; or on darker nights by the starlight of searchlights, the whitish beams of masked torches, the blue lamps of the incident officer, and emphasized by here and there a red hurricane lamp lit to advise a roadblock. In such cold light, with the pale plaster crumbled out on the street, with the puppety figures of rescue workers in their flat bowlerish hats covered also with pale dust, with the dead and wounded collapsed and unmoving—there was some of the atmosphere of the doll-shop, the shop for making plaster figures or people of wax. There would be an emptiness in the late-night street, with a strange and inhuman scurrying round one broken house. Part of the character of a human crowd is the sense of different directions, of all people going their own way; but here in the emptiness suddenly the crowd worked together—and became a crowd of puppets. Thus the scene from outside: inside lived the human breath. But standing aloof, or coming up upon such a scene, there was the mood of a plaster workshop—and strangely a feeling of creation rather than of destruction.

Of the other, the firelit scene, a simple thing can be said—that it looked theatrical. In the reddish fireglow, or by the enormous yellow glare of a burning gas main, faces became painted, the scene a garish set-piece. Here a pantomime was afoot, in the empty street a sudden festival booth had been erected and the play was on. At the root of this appearance lies something of the sympathy between *grand guignol* and the clown. Both, though one may laugh, are festivals of the macabre, of torchlit painted terror.

Such scenes, the cold and the fiery, were both to return now to London, in the January of 1944.

Towards the end of 1943 the incidence of single raiders had increased. For some time what is said to have been the most formidable anti-aircraft barrage in the world had been disposed around and throughout London. Of this concentrated armament the most spectacular new device was an emission of rocket projectiles that, disgorged in square formation and in hundreds at one time, rose from the ground in a many-tailed flight of fire and with a mighty whooosh—to enclose high up in a box of blast and splinters the invading German aircraft. On some nights in 1943 these rockets were heard, and their attendant gunfire of various calibre and resonance: but it was not until the German pilots returned in some force in January that the full orchestra of this barrage was heard in fortissimo concert.

For Westminster the Little Blitz, as this period of from January to April came to be called, began on 19th January. The raids were concentrated, they seemed to single out a particular district in a way that was unusual during the previous raiding period. Westminster was given the attention of the Luftwaffe on some seven nights, and in varying degrees of concentration. In between these, as other parts of London received their sharp attacks, the nights were alert and noisy. The reason for this return of the Luftwaffe was held to be an answer to the heavy saturation raids made on Germany by British and American airfleets; they may also have been aimed at disturbing the southward movement of our armies towards the tip of the springboard on the channel coast.

To describe in general the feeling of the period, one might best return to words written then:

'In the first days of air-raids, when raids lasted the whole night through, they dominated life in the city, so that people were more prepared for them and met them with a composure, if indeed unhappily engendered, that rose to combat the expected. Raids consumed a great proportion of the hours of the day by which people measure time. But now into a day of twenty-four hours the raid bursts suddenly, twists and prods its hot barb for only one vicious hour—and then there is silence. There has been a terrible interruption, but it was no more than that, an interruption, an alien force disturbing and accelerating the normal pace of things. . . .

'. . . (People) readjusted themselves to the pace of the working day.

So it was with the rest of the city, except for isolated patches occurring suddenly round some street corners, where astonishing heaps of glass lay about the gutters and torn curtains flapped forlornly over their world of broken brick and plaster. Yet in these patches, dead and desolate, occurring suddenly and bounded then again by more acres of the unconcerned city, rescuers were tunnelling throughout the days beneath creaking debris, little cries no louder than a baby's sob might be heard muffled through the terrible laths and plaster—and at the next corner a man arrives suddenly with a barrowful of oranges, a crowd queues from nowhere, the oranges are gone!'

Thus the isolated incident round the corner. But on several occasions the damage became more concentrated, and a whole area was affected, and over many streets there hung the feeling of the first bad days. The first of such more concentrated nights in Westminster was the 22nd January, when after increasing activity in the previous weeks, German aircraft delivered a sharp but limited incendiary attack in the neighbourhood of the Houses of Parliament.

It became a night of excitement and of rumour. Incendiaries littered Parliament Square, New Scotland Yard, and the surrounding Embankment area. Buildings along one side of the Square were alight, and their firelight flashed on the windows of the Houses of Parliament, causing observers from afar to believe that the seat of government was again alight. In fact it was: but the fire was limited to Westminster Hall, where there had developed a difficult situation in the roof among the ancient wooden beams. However, fire-fighting services were quickly mobilized and concentrated here; once again the Hall was saved and the initial damage kept from spreading far in the roof.

Meanwhile another fire had started in Cannon Row police station. A Firepot Bomb was dropped into the Council's Depot in Pimlico and another in the roadway outside. The first lodged in an electric vehicle, and was extinguished, while the second produced a warden's report: 'The first time that IBs were noted burning like tulips in the roadway.' This effect of little sprouts of flower-like flame was caused by the Firepot's habit of exploding in the air and scattering its incendiary material down on to the streets and roofs.

In the war's perspective, this fire-raid can be counted a small affair—in terms of bulk. But in terms of feeling its effect was profound. Such a raid represented an unknown quantity. The firelight flickering in the Houses of Parliament mirrored in those windows a deep apprehension. Was it to be the first of Germany's revenge raids of saturation? Were such incendiaries the flare-path for an annihilation of high explosives? Was this the beginning again of the old misery, the cold long nights of dust and fear and fire, the resumption of the past? Little was known to the man in the street of Germany's air potential. Much was anticipated. It seemed only common sense that a country as proud and savage would not remain sitting under the huge weight of fire delivered from these shores at that time. Revenge had been threatened on the Deutschlandsender. Here—for all one could think—it was. So the City held its breath and waited. Miraculously, after about an hour, the All Clear left its relieved silence in the wide night sky.

But if the blow never fell, the threat remained. Almost nightly the alert was sounded and the barrage bluffed the dark with its tremendous noise. Generally, nerves were at their lowest ebb for the whole war. People suffered from the old illusion—that having once been hit they had 'taken it' and were not eligible for a further dose. And here was the same experience to be faced all over again. It was depressing. And though the wide military field was at an optimistic high, there were now several years of exhaustive work and short rations to further lower the nervous resistance. So the shelters were filled again, and though the bombing was never as severe as had been apprehended, attacks were savage and their effect demoralizing out of proportion to their weight. This is not to say that the London morale had lost its old obduracy: it merely records that now people were more tired, that hopes of an earlier invasion were postponed, and that generally the perverse vivacities and the do-or-die ebullience of the old Blitz were not so evident. This Little Blitz was a glum business. The nerves were impatient of it.

However, in the practical field of Civil Defence the intensive training and reorganization of the past years proved undeniably their efficacy. The new raids were dealt with ably and quickly. There was, in fact, a certain nonchalance in the smooth working of these affairs. The question of emergency water supplies for the Fire Service had been vastly improved: there was proved in practice the Wardens' system of one commanding Incident officer with his subsidiary officers' posts and incident inquiry posts manned by the Women's Voluntary Service. The work of inspiring these new developments in Civil Defence and the work of carrying them out in the long hours of training—these were now justified. As it was, training even continued during the raiding period—with such an intensity, for instance, that during certain high pressure courses two instructors helping the Assistant Staff Officer fell asleep on their feet. And once more, then, the popularity of the various Civil Defence operatives rose in the public estimation.

New weapons had to be dealt with. There was the Firepot Bomb, a mixture of explosive (17 pounds) and thermite incendiaries. There were several types of anti-personnel and otherwise explosive incendiary bombs, each a danger from up to about 30 to 50 yards. There were phosphorus bombs of 50 kg. and 250 kg., each containing phosphorus oil and rubber that spattered out stickily over an area of up to 20 or 30 yards, igniting spontaneously, and liable if temporarily quenched to reignite when again dried. Added to these incendiary and anti-personnel devices were the advances made in the quality of high explosive itself, and of fusing machinery: small bombs had now a far fiercer effect than three years previously.

Then, although fortunately London saw few of these, there were the Butterfly bombs. They were small delayed-action explosive anti-personnel devices equipped with 'wings' that might catch in roofs or other protuberances, or lie quiescent on the ground. They could be actuated by a person treading the ground nearby. Such sensitivity represented their greatest danger to reconnaissance parties. On an occasion they were dropped in quantities in the Grimsby district, and there caused an annoyance of some dimension to the defence forces.

These small explosives might have caused a serious dislocation if dropped in numbers over a city area, and their anticipation caused the authorities much concern. A special poster campaign was run by the Home Office to illustrate their particular dangers. But fortunately the Butterflies never arrived. It was thought in retrospect that perhaps with only a small airfleet at their disposal the Germans found it more efficient to devote carrying-loads to the bombs that would affect the material city that was their real target: anti-personnel devices might have caused dislocation, but only of a temporary kind. In the same way, this might have been the reason for the very limited use of anti-personnel incendiaries—in that an explosive device usually reduced the thermite content, the first reason for the bomb, by half.

After the January fire-raid there was in the Westminster district a month of alert but little action. Then on the nights of February 19th, 20th, 23rd and 24th the attention of the raiders returned.

The 19th was notable for a high explosive that struck a house in Queen's Gate, then occupied by the *Institut de France à Londres*. The bomb fell some time after midnight, demolished the front wall of the building and damaged the adjoining house. At the same time other bombs fell in the roadway fracturing water and gas mains, and setting up a flame. Fire then developed in the house adjoining the French Institute and soon spread—for the Fire Service was temporarily handicapped by lack of water, with mains dry and the nearest static tank soon emptied. With its front wall fallen out, the interior of the building looked like a stage. Rescue parties could be seen working up through the floors. One man in an upper story was pinned in bed with a beam across him: he was first thought to be dead, but when rescuers lifted the beam—then in the words of an officer watching this tragic theatre from the street: 'He was off down the ladder like a scalded cat.' Others were less fortunate, for the deaths of six persons and the serious wounding of some eight others resulted from the incident.

Otherwise, a major fire was caused in a large furniture depository in Lupus Street. Packed furniture burns fiercely, avidly, as firewood burns in a grate. Despite this, and though the building itself was destroyed, the Fire Service were successful in limiting the fire and particularly in saving its spread to one of Pimlico's danger spots, a display service store full of inflammable material.

This night also saw the first incidence of phosphorus bombs in Westminster. One bomb of 50 kilo weight fell on the roof of the Fortress, the concrete summit of the underground extension to the War Office, and there burnt out in the centre doing no damage whatsoever to the roof. Several other of these bombs fell in various places. In some cases fire developed and was extinguished: unignited phosphorus was disposed of with wet sand and craters were cleaned up by 'firing' the next day. It had been known that the Germans were dropping phosphorus incendiaries—and people were particularly aware of this after the extensive phosphorus attacks that the Allied airfleets were delivering on Axis towns. This night saw Westminster's first practical introduction to them. Not much harm was done. But the raid was memorable for its excitement, properly expressed by the report of one civilian who said he had seen a phosphorus bomb fall and on being asked how he knew, said: 'Because it *glared* at me when I looked round the corner.'

On the next night four high explosives hit the Whitehall area, two on the Horse Guards Parade, one on the nearby pigeon house in St. James's Park, and one in Whitehall by the Treasury. The latter bomb killed five people and injured others: the stone facing to the Treasury was pocked and torn and the building blasted but not substantially damaged. Downing Street suffered blast from one of the Horse Guards Parade bombs, and a patrolling warden received the freak gift of two bomb splinters, one in his leg and the other in his greatcoat pocket. Minor damage was done to the building surrounding the Parade, to the Admiralty, Horse Guards building, Scottish Office and War Office.

Meanwhile the night was sharp with incendiaries, and several fires were started. The magazine in Hyde Park was alight, with some ammunition exploding, and there were fires in Pall Mall and elsewhere, though no serious situation developed at any of these places.

However, grave damage did occur in the Pall Mall vicinity on the next raiding night, the night of the 23rd February, when a stick of four high explosives caused damage over an area of six acres between Jermyn Street and Pall Mall. These four bombs, falling in a line so that the blast of each overlapped the other, created a complicated situation disproportionate to the weight of the individual bombs themselves. In the first place, a wardens' post was demolished and patrolling wardens killed—so that the immediate staff most acquainted with the area, together with their records, were unavailable. In all, four wardens were killed; but others who were buried and temporarily shocked managed to extricate themselves and, regardless of their personal predicament, carried on.

Several gas and water mains were broken. Fire flamed up from the debris. And the field of destruction was so mazed and widespread that for a time, though rescue parties arrived promptly at the main centres of damage, no absolute control was possible.

But the stunned interval was momentary, soon the District Warden had arrived and assumed control as incident officer and soon after the Chief Warden came personally from the Report Centre. An incident officer's post and two sub-posts were eventually set up—and this is important particularly because thereafter the incident, complicated as it was, proved beyond doubt the efficacy of the new control system, the absolute command of an incident by one man. It became a classic example of how an area of damage should successfully be run. And here again, in a district where many small houses and commercial premises were affected, there was proved the use of the Incident Inquiry Point, which, in this case, answered some 8,000 inquiries and remained open for as long as nine days.

The terrain covered a built-up area of mostly eighteenth-century brick buildings, together with groups of small houses probably three hundred years old and certain other modern reinforced buildings. The oldest of these, centred in three enclosed yards or courts between King Street and Pall Mall, suffered most heavily. However, blast damage extended from Cleveland Square below St. James's along the north-easterly run of the bombs up to Jermyn Street above Ormond Yard: laterally, the blast travelled as far as Arthur's Club in St. James's and the Carlton Club in Pall Mall. The southernmost bomb fell in Pall Mall itself opposite a taxidermist's establishment, scattering a disquietening heterogeny of stuffed beasts into the street. The northernmost struck part of the London Library and destroyed many valuable records and books. The two central bombs fell one in the old court called Pall Mall place, demolishing many of the small houses there and in Rose and Crown Yard; and the other fell on the Duke Street corner of King Street, demolishing that corner, destroying such aristocratic neighbours as the Orleans club, and blasting far and wide art treasures and jewellery from premises nearby.

The area was roped off by the police, and owners of property only permitted within on ticket of entry specially and personally issued. Apart from the necessity of keeping the area free for civil defence movement, many thousands of pounds' worth of valuables were thrown widely over the debris and the littered streets. Despite all precautions looting did occur: but in the circumstances, it was limited. And eventually, after weeks of salvage work, upwards of half a million pounds' worth of valuables were recovered. This Pall Mall incident was the worst that Westminster suffered during the Little Blitz. Forty-eight persons were injured and nine killed.

On the following night a further fire-raising raid was attempted, though on a small scale. The busiest area was Soho. Fires were started in Wardour Street and three high explosives fell in the neighbourhood, though with few casualties. In Old Compton Street a freak of London post-Blitz architecture was born. In the shadow of St. Anne's sad but beautiful ruin there ran along the southern side of the street a row of shops, centred on a narrow-fronted public-house. Previously shops to the east of the pub had been demolished, leaving the pub-wall rising naked and sheer for all its untouched stories: now the building to the west was struck—and again all was ripped down short of the western pub-wall, leaving the building thus standing unscathed, tall and thin in the centre of nothing.

A gas main was alight opposite, a mound of brown earth steamed where a small club, fortunately unfilled at that time, had been accommodated: up Wardour Street firemen trailed their hoses among dressmakers' dummies; on the trees in St. Anne's churchyard hung a tattering of scarecrow garments blasted from a second-hand clothier's. The Prime Minister arrived and talked with rescuers and rescued. It was a cold February night: firelight, water on the streets, a woman sobbing dark in a doorway, a great kernel of activity gradually decreasing as the incident was cleared and the night wore on.

Then a respite until March, when on the 14th a sharp and rather heavier incendiary raid was delivered. Phosphorus was again used, mixed with a few explosives. And again the few explosives were curiously reinforced by isolated 1,000 kilo bombs, unexploded. This time there were two of these, against single bombs on several of the previous raid nights; but they fell innocently enough in Hyde Park and in a square off Knightsbridge.

The amount of incendiaries distinguished the raid—firebombs of many sorts and sizes were dropped in bulk; firebombs in containers, or singly, with or without explosive, and in large proportion fired by the phosphorus agent. A number of these broke or failed otherwise to ignite, and the morning saw the City's Cleansing Department on the job of disposal. Several large fires were started, including those at the Burdett-Coutts School coupled with a paint store in Rochester Row, St. Philip's Church in Flask Lane, the Council's Depot in Monck Street; and the largest—a twenty-pump fire—involving the Church of the Sacred Heart in Medway Street, the Westminster Training College and a timber store belonging to the Office of Works. All these fires were successfully extinguished, together with smaller ones nipped in the bud by the Fire Service or by the army of civilian fire-guards. Such a fire-raising raid that in earlier days might have provoked a serious fire situation was by prompt and organized action turned to failure. The night was otherwise notable in that only two casualties were suffered in the whole City. One of these was fatal—a woman was killed by a piece of masonry thrown some distance from an explosive that landed in Cliveden Place.

This unlucky woman was to be the last victim of these piloted raids of early 1944. There were other alerts, parachute flares and anti-aircraft shells dropped on the City, and on one night a few fires were begun in the Strand district. But no more major damage was done.

The City remained alert, and increasingly so. For, although again it seemed to the more optimistic that raids had again exhausted themselves, nevertheless talk of the coming invasion of the Continent grew stronger. And with the invasion raids were expected, raids perhaps of a kind that London had not yet known. Saturation attacks? Gas? Heavy raids on the ports and thus an evacuation inland to London . . . and then raids to harry the evacuated? Or—a counter-invasion? All these possibilities and their permutations were catered for. Civil Defenders had tasted again the savoury snack of action, they were proved efficient and stood on the top line. They trained harder. They waited. They heard that all military leave was cancelled. They heard that it was granted again. The days passed, the weeks. They waited.

On June 6th General Eisenhower's message came through. Allied forces had landed in Normandy. The Invasion—the Second Front— was on. That morning there were at first cheers, relief, the impulse to wave flags. But by noon the streets were strangely hushed. People went about their business anxiously and quietly, straining their eyes to the placards, waiting impatiently for the news. Public-houses, for instance, were far emptier than usual. People went home—to wait. Everyone knew, with a heaviness in their hearts, that the day involved the lives of all those men in uniform with whom they had rubbed nonchalant shoulders in the City's streets during the previous weeks, months, years. That day saw a death of smiles in London, as they knew it was a death abroad of the smiles that ghosted then the empty streets.

Secondly a heaviness of apprehension weighed like a cloud from the sky itself—for Londoners were again bracing themselves to receive what they might expect. No one took the German lightly. There was a myth of German armed might that died uneasily, there was a reality of German offensive power that citizens themselves remembered. Now again they looked warily at the silent skies. Through the past years they had grown used to looking upwards. It is in passing a peculiarity of the war that people in a city raised their eyes more to the roofs and above than ever before; they discovered and grew to know the contours of the upper parts of buildings and changing textures in the skies that they had never known to exist before. Now, the upward eye was seen squinting again through the quiet London of 6th June.

Nothing happened.

And the news from Normandy was good. Relief set in, gradually. But in the posts and depots of the Civil Defence forces there was allowed no relaxation. Vehicles were kept tuned to a pitch, various privileges of short leave were forsworn. And again, despite their known efficiency and the known need for them, members of Civil Defence found themselves suddenly again at zero in the public esteem. Memories were short-lived, emotions were immediate, imagination non-existent. It had become suddenly evident to the armchair critic of the street-corner that overnight all A.R.P. personnel should have been transformed magically into trained khaki at the touch of a fairy baton. In so few days the City's danger seemed to have receded, the need for its defenders and nurses grown obsolete. But in a few more days' time the armchairs were wheeling merrily again to shelter.

On the 13th June the first flying-bomb landed in London—in Bethnal Green. At first this was thought to be a piloted aircraft shot down. An inquest was held, and the ensuing days were to reveal the advent of a new weapon. On the night of the 15th June the sirens sounded a general alert at a few minutes past half-past eleven. The all-clear was not heard until half-past nine on the following morning. During this period the first flying-bombs were seen from Westminster. They were not known then for what they were. In the night sky they appeared as a travelling light on the tail of a fast-moving aircraft. Very heavy gunfire followed the light as it bulleted along. Sometimes it seemed to the general watcher from the street or the roofs to be a German fighter-bomber with its tail alight: thus the first flights, and the distant red bursts of flame as the engine stopped, raised a cheer in the streets—it seemed to be good firing and another Jerry brought to earth.

But see the report from the Westminster Wardens' Operations Office for June 15th and 16th:

'No incidents were reported but gunfire was heavy at times and it appeared that some new form of attack was in progress.

'The Chief Warden and his Assistant Operations Officer visited the site of one of the larger incidents[1] this morning and, as a result of this inspection and from discussions with Bomb Disposal Officers and other Civil Defence personnel, have drawn the following conclusions:

1. That the missile being used by the enemy is a Pilotless Aircraft.

2. That there is no evidence as yet as to how the missile is discharged.

3. The missile causes a very small crater and its effect is almost entirely blast.

4. The area of blast damage is extensive with a centre of damage of anything up to 200 yards in which old type buildings of three stories were entirely demolished up to a radius of 100 yards.

5. So far but few fires have been caused by the missiles and no UX specimens have as yet been recovered.'

Thus the character of the new arrival was pieced together from evidence on the spot, from previous speculation, from intelligence reports circulated from the respective ministries. From the early morning of the 16th June onwards the attack started in earnest, with bombs arriving constantly by day and by night, with the first long alert periods developing into many irregular short soundings of the siren, and with heavy gunfire following each bomb. On the 18th the gunfire ceased. Ring defences had been established outside the built-up area of London. And on the 18th, too, at about ten to nine o'clock in the morning the first

[1] Not in Westminster.

fly-bomb descended on Westminster. There rose into the air above the roof-tops the first giant plume of dust that was to be the mark of these explosions.

The bomb fell on residential property in Rutherford Street, killing ten people and injuring sixty-two others. A dangerous fire developed but was got under control and the incident as a whole presented no notable difficulties, though it was the first practical experience and though naturally the damage was widespread. But a few hours later, at twenty minutes past eleven, there occurred one of the most serious tragedies of the period—the direct destruction of the Guards' Chapel attached to Wellington Barracks.

It was a Sunday morning—a grey morning, cloudy, as so many others were to be—and at the time a short service was in progress: had the bomb fallen twenty minutes before or after, the chapel would have been empty of the large congregation then assembled. As it was, one hundred and nineteen persons were killed and one hundred and two were seriously injured: though nevertheless no fewer than one hundred and forty-one escaped from that dreadfully enclosed space at least with their lives.

The bomb roared down over the high black shape of Queen Anne's Mansions, and then fell almost vertically, onto the roof of the gun-grey chapel. The roof and heavy concrete girders collapsed instantly and fell down inside on the congregation who were then listening to the reading of the lesson.

To a first aid party that soon arrived the scene in its subsiding dust looked vast and boxlike, impenetrable; sloping masses of the grey walls and roof shut in the wounded: the doors were blocked, the roof crammed down; it was difficult to find any entrance: but there was one—behind the altar. From then on it became a matter for nurses and doctors to scramble up and down and in between the large intractable slopes and walls of chunked concrete—the same as perhaps in a low-tide rock formation, but here gritty and powdered everywhere with the lung-choking dust. These rocks of material had to be manhandled off casualties. While doctors were plugging morphia and nurses and first aid personnel were feeding bicarbonate solution and wrapping on mine-dressings, all rescue services together with soldiers from the barracks began prising up the debris-blocks and carrying out those freed.

At that time the King's Guard had just dismounted and were waiting for dismissal in the barrack square. There were thus extra hands on the spot, and a regular military liaison was set up in conjunction with other services. Outside in Birdcage Walk a Mobile Aid Unit had driven up.

Nurses also dealt with wounded in an undemolished room at the end of the chapel. An Incident Inquiry point again dealt with the many inquiries that resulted from this catastrophe, of such large scale and involving so many prominent personages. Finally, notwithstanding its large amount, the debris was all removed and the last body recovered within forty-eight hours.

From then onwards the flying-bombs bombarded London regularly. In all, over a period from the 18th June to the 27th August, thirty struck within the Westminster City limits, together with fourteen boundary incidents where blast was suffered.

Their total effect was to kill 267 people, seriously injure 663, and to wound upwards of 1,000 others. They caused in addition very great damage, both in the demolition of buildings near their immediate striking point and also particularly in the extensive reach of the outer blast area, where roofs and glass windows, the prerequisites of elemental shelter, suffered heavily. On the other hand, since the bombs exploded most sensitively upon impact, there was little penetration of the roadway or dislocation of underground utility services, though cables could be stretched by the indirect rocking of the ground: but generally the bogey of broken gas and water mains was non-existent. Fire damage amounted to little and proved only incident upon an inflammation setting up within the debris.

The bombs fell without direction, and many struck open roadways and parks, causing few casualties. When they struck built-up areas, the rate of death and particularly of injury rose high. The Guards Chapel incident was remarkable for its high proportion of deaths. At the other end of the scale came the daylight occurrence on the roof of the Regent Palace Hotel, a few yards off Piccadilly Circus, where only one person was killed and 168 injured: the average for the whole period in Westminster is computed at 9·2 persons killed per bomb and 22·8 seriously injured. This may be compared with 0·71 killed and 1·21 injured per exploded bomb of the original Blitz in 1940–41.

An interesting reflection on Westminster behaviour during this period is mirrored in comparative figures quoted for the fly-bombing of such cities as Antwerp and Liége. These were most heavily attacked from the field when occupied by the Allied Armies. In Antwerp 3·5 people were killed per flying-bomb, and in Liége only 1·1 died, and Liége received as many as *one thousand flying-bombs in two months*. Though conditions are not fairly comparable, the general inference to be drawn is that in Liége the people lived throughout that period in their shelters. In Westminster, hit more lightly, though threatened by many hundreds of bombs falling short and passing overhead, the people took surprisingly little shelter and persisted about their daily business on the streets, in their places of work and in their homes.

The period of pilotless attack on London continued until the 28th March, when the last flying-bomb came over at breakfast time: after this the various launching sites removed to Holland were over-run—and the long months of arbitrary death were finished. By far the worst part of this period may be remembered as June and the beginning of July. Then the defences were experimental and German launching sites were mostly localized at near range in the Pas de Calais. The bombs came over singly or in bursts of several. Usually they followed a regular course, so that citizens of London had engraved in their minds an imaginative conception of air-lanes, like rail-tracks in the sky, along which the regular bombs sped. Sometimes, though, they deviated from their set course, swinging round in a final curve, even circling or diving straight to earth with a full and terrifying roar.

In the first months, though the bombardment continued ceaselessly, certain times of the day became rather more popular with the German firing command: between eight o'clock and nine in the morning when people were going to work, and at lunchtime, and at eleven o'clock on Sunday morning when either church or the morning stroll might find people congregated or on the streets. To add to the foreboding of those first weeks of concentrated danger, the weather remained changeless—rain and low clouds. It continued so all through June, and for the first part of July: it seemed almost a concomitant tactic, the result of some comprehensive German control of the weather. So different from the clear summer weather of the Wehrmacht's spring offensives, the dull weather proved a complete cover for these winged stiletto-like missiles that evaded thus our gunfire and our eyes. Few but those flying low were easily seen; all one heard was the loudly fanning noise; the bombs might thus always have been just overhead. That kind of weather, too, punctured the spirit's resilience: it had, in fact, the usual glum effect of close, wet, cloudy weather. June to the Englishman is mystically 'flaming June': he has been bred to believe in this, and he never learns. So that altogether, apart from a minority who flew fascinated to the rooftops to see what they could with their own eyes, the mood of London sank low: though, as has been said, a momentary sunken spirit never seemed much to affect the obduracy of the day's work and the daily life. People did not like being put out, and they seldom were: until the bomb itself forced them.

Flying-bombs were particularly disliked for their automatic nature, their unpleasant unreality. It was difficult to imagine a machine flying by itself: it was easier to picture a kind of grim steel automatic pilot cast in the shape of a man, flying straight, freeing the last control with a sightless jerk of his arm. Such nightmares came easily to a people removed from centuries of superstition by only a few years. The new things were supernatural. The idea of a grey-clad pilot with Nazi-blond hair seemed almost affectionate in comparison. But in addition to such a concrete vision, a curious psychological situation evolved—for this was the first time in their lives that people had been faced with a *purely arbitrary fate*. Hitherto, every bombardment might at least be thought to have had a target, a direction: and there had always been contrary devices to deflect the attack. But here in these first days (and this feeling was to develop further with the Long-Range Rocket) the sound of a flying-bomb approached like a straight line, so that everybody in the half-circle of its fanning-forward sound attached the bomb to themselves and knew that without any particular reason it could drop at any time and any place. It could drop anywhere. It was absolutely reasonless, the first purely fatal agent that had come to man for centuries, tempting him to cross his fingers again, bringing a rebirth of superstition.

Lastly, in more material mind, the people saw this as destruction at its most wanton. Now they could see no possible excuse of military targets. Homes, women, children and old people were openly the slaughter-toys of the German. So a grim fury was generated that to an extent must have recuperated the shocked spirits of a people who now, after all they had suffered, were faced with renewed and fiercer attack, with a Secret Weapon (the war of nerves was not altogether unsuccessful) and an unpredictable future. There was always, too, the thought to sustain the spirit of the land battles in France. People thought that even though this was bad, there was worse being endured over the other side.

So life continued. Flying glass was the worst danger, and people were told to take the nearest cover on the sound of the bomb diving or of the engine cutting out. So they continued their work or their walk until this last moment, when they ducked to the ground or behind the nearest obstruction. As time went on, an 'imminent warning' system was brought in. A klaxon horn was the most usual device, and as the streets resounded to its prolonged croak, as the noise of a distant bomb hurried forward its crescendo, people in offices all over the City were shepherded into the passages—away at all costs from *glass*. That was right, for in material terms the effect over a square quarter-mile of blast was simply that of two or three thousand war-drunk savages rising from ambush and flinging wildly their assegais in all directions.

In the very first days, some offices and factories ordered their staffs down to basement shelters on the sounding of the siren. But this grew to be so frequent that, even if the dislocation of work had not mattered, people nevertheless became tired of the stairs and all the trouble and preferred to remain seated and to chance matters. They were given an internal warning bell system operated by a spotter on the roof. He in his turn judged the moment from the district warning telephoned from observer posts and the Air Ministry plotting service, or more intimately from the black socks that were run up on gallows erected on all high roofs. On the sound of this bell, office staffs trooped off into the corridors, waited, sometimes crouched, and then trooped back.

Most flying-bombs fell in the southern districts and then in gradually declining quantity northwards to the River. Many southern boroughs, such as Croydon and Lewisham, suffered very badly during the period of this attack: for them the experience was certainly on a level, if not worse, than the most severe days of the 1940-1 Blitz. In this regard, the experience of Westminster cannot reflect the full measure of anguish that the flying-bomb brought to parts of London: but although the City never actually received the great weight of attack, nevertheless the air echoed constantly the threat of the bombs' approaching sound, the urgent throb of a two-stroke motor-cycle engine amplified thunderously and scuttling at four hundred miles an hour—and the Westminster day was ominous with those frequent explosions beyond the southern bank of the Thames. Many, too, flew over the City and reached as far north as the Midlands. Thirty struck the city, ringed as it was with explosives also in neighbouring boroughs.

The effects of the new weapon determined new tactics for the forces of Civil Defence. There were three main technical advantages occasioned by these incidents over previous types of bombing, though they were offset by a multitude of new troubles. First, the bombs could be seen by high-placed observer posts both by day and by night (excepting those days of particularly low, obfuscating cloud): so that the position of their fall could be judged and reported very quickly in terms of an accurate vicinity report which could name the particular building hit in a matter of thirty seconds, either by night or by day. Secondly, the incidents themselves were in Westminster usually isolated, so that services could be deployed in force to the one area without the constant coming and going of the old days. Thirdly, there were no penetrative troubles with the utility systems under the road: and there was little fire.

However, despite these consolations new and disturbing dangers were to be faced. In the first place, Westminster was faced with a deluge of free casualties such as it had never before known, except perhaps in the case of mines. Hitherto Rescue Services had been used to a high proportion of *trapped* casualties. Speed in the setting up of control and the assembling of first aid and other immediate rescue services became a first essential. The National Fire Service, accustomed according to its lights to turn out at express speed, had decided to send a convoy of pumps and a turntable ladder to all flying-bomb incidents—and this convoy therefore was liable to assemble at the debris in advance of other civil defence services: an advance of perhaps 3—5 minutes against 15—20 minutes.

So that these considerations determined the formation by Westminster Civil Defence of a system of Flying Columns. The complement of these fluctuated, but at one average time they were comprised of two Heavy Rescue lorries, two Light Rescue vehicles, two ambulances (or four by day) and a Mobile Aid Post. The expedition was so devised as to be on the scene of damage in three minutes. Their turn out from the depots was synchronized with the despatch from City Hall Headquarters of a Flying Column car containing an Incident Officer to take charge, the Chief Warden's Staff Officer or Assistant accompanied by an Assistant District Rescue Officer, and a Staff Officer of the Light Rescue. As the situation developed, this Headquarters car was augmented by District Incident Officers who were appointed specially for the purpose in each of the six City districts. These in turn were assisted by a Post Incident Officer and the nearest available team of wardens.

Flying Columns were ordered out from the Control Centre, as advised by Vicinity Reports from various agencies. Of these there was, for instance, the Wardens' Observer Post situated in the high modernist concrete tower of the Victoria Coach Station. From here an unobstructed view could be obtained over the City, and observation reached a high pitch of efficiency. And among other such observer posts figured the Air Ministry's system placed on top of the London Transport offices in Broadway, and the National Fire Service's observation posts of which one was situated on the summit of the Regent Palace Hotel at Piccadilly Circus. Vicinity reports were also despatched expressly from local Wardens' Posts.

Other operational changes included the use of a loudspeaker van to control crowds that tended to obstruct seriously the mobility of ambu-

lances and rescue vehicles. Dogs were used now on occasions in reconnaissance of the inner debris. Because there were no German eyes above,
the use of artificial lighting at night was less restricted and searchlights
now aided rescue work. The great area of damage increased the need
for personnel to make a complete reconnaissance as early as possible;
and it was found propitious to bring as many facilities to the incident
as possible, rather than make the persons affected go to the facilities—
thus the use of kerbside meals, mobile bath and laundry units was
extended. Special district furniture officers were appointed to attend
all incidents, for furniture removal was now to take an important place
in post-raid procedure. First Aid Repair squads were also despatched
early to the perimeter of the damage—for beside the widespread wounding of people by splinters there was a widespread wounding of
windows and roof-tiles, these houses needed to be healed, for there
existed nowhere sufficient alternative accommodation for the large
evacuations that would otherwise have been caused. As it was, the
main attack took place in the warm weather, and families were not
over-discomforted by a short period of draughty windows before repairs
could be made.

Thus in the desolate dusty area of blast hammers echoed, draught-
proof material was nailed over the window-frames, tarpaulins were
suspended on damaged roofs. To the tune of the hammering more
bombs flew over. And meanwhile from less habitable houses all services
that could be spared were removing furniture and possessions, shaking
away the dust and packing them off in vans to the quick-filling City
furniture stores.

People took to the shelters again at night. Or if they remained at
home placed furniture or blankets between their sleeping faces and the
glass windows. Awake, when the room filled with the sudden rosy glare
that flashed when the bomb's engine stopped, they pulled the bedclothes over their faces and waited. One . . . two . . . three . . . four
seconds and either the windows came flying in or they didn't.

Bombs that struck home in Westminster in June landed in or on the
following buildings and areas, in this order, as from 18th June: Carey
Mansions in Rutherford Street (10 killed, 62 wounded);[1] The Guards'
Chapel in Wellington Barracks (119 killed, 141 wounded); Clements
Inn (3 killed, 12 wounded); Constitution Hill (1 wounded); Wilfred
Street (9 killed, 60 wounded); Victoria Station (14 killed, 68 wounded);
Peabody Buildings in Wild Street (2 killed, 17 wounded); Regent
Palace Hotel Annexe in Brewer Street (1 killed, 168 wounded); Ald-

[1] 'Wounded' includes those seriously concussed by blast.

wych, opposite N.E. wing of Bush House (46 killed, 399 wounded); Winchester Street (13 killed, 150 wounded).

And in July: Peabody Avenue (7 killed, 85 wounded); Tufton Street (3 killed, 29 wounded); Westmorland Terrace (10 killed, 62 wounded); River Thames opposite Charing Cross Underground station (2 wounded); Conduit Street (15 wounded); Monck Street, by the Rotunda (20 casualties); River Thames opposite Millbank (7 minor casualties); Electra House (2 killed, 17 wounded); Hyde Park at the Dell (2 killed, 12 wounded); Buckingham Palace grounds near Wellington Arch (2 wounded); Ebury Buildings (65 wounded); River Thames near Charing Cross station (8 wounded); Milford Lane (5 killed, 15 wounded); Grosvenor Road (33 wounded).

And in August: Tullet Place, Brompton Road (6 killed, 21 wounded); Cursitor Street (2 wounded); Lansdowne House (6 killed, 36 wounded); Hyde Park, by the Nursery (no casualties); Vincent Street (9 killed, 26 wounded); Hyde Park near the Bathing Pavilion (1 wounded).

The worst day of all began at midday on the 30th June, when four bombs fell in fifteen hours, including both the Aldwych Incident and that at the Regent Palace Hotel. In those fifteen hours sixty-seven were killed and 802 wounded. However, in contrast to such high casualty rates six bombs falling in the parks and other depopulated spaces together wounded no more than some ten people. It may be noted that the Strand district suffered most, receiving altogether six flying-bombs and the blast of others.

Rather than investigate the detail of each incident, which could not help but make monotonous history, three different types of incident are annotated in the following pages. First, however, to give some picture of the typical scene, a few lines written at the time may be quoted, lines written after the Conduit Street incident.

'Drove swiftly through the quiet Sunday streets. Sometimes at odd corners or through a breach in the skyline of tall buildings the huge buff plume showed itself, calm and clean as sand against a pale bluish sky. Then, gradually, the immaculate polish showed a ruffling, stray scraps of paper suggested the passing of a crowd, a weed of splintered glass sprung up here and there on the pavements, another and invisible weed seemed to be thrusting the window frames from their sockets and ahead, as this tangle grew denser, the street hung fogged with yellow dust.

'Our destination lay within the dust. Once inside it was easy to see, only the outer air had painted it opaque. But it was like driving from the streets of a town into sudden country; nothing metropolitan remained to these torn pavements, to the earthen mortar dust and the shattered brick returning to the clay. The fly-bomb had blasted a pause within the pause of Sunday morning.

'Ambulances already. Two or three people stood about, handkerchiefs to their red-splashed faces. But we were ordered round the debris to search the broken buildings on either side.

'At the top of the first flight of stairs, dark and rickety, a light shone through a crack in the unhinged door. The door came off easily. A single shadeless electric bulb hung over a tailor's table, shone weakly and yellow against the large daylit window beyond. On the table lay a pair of trousers, an iron, slivers of glass and splashes of red blood, comet-shaped, like flickings from a pen. Every lightly fixed furnishing of the room had shifted—bales of cloth, doors, chairs, plaster mouldings, a tall cupboard—all these had moved closer and now leant huddled at strange, intimate angles. Plaster dust covered everything. There was no space left in the room, there was nobody in the room. The blood led in wide round drops to the door, the tailor must have been "walking wounded". Had he been one of those outside, fingering blindly for the ambulance doors? The yellow bulb on its single string burned on, the only life in this lonely Sunday workroom, the only relic of the tailor's shattered patience.

'Then, under the steady burning of this bulb, against its silent continuing effort, other sounds began to whisper. Our boots had thudded on the stairs. Now for a moment, no more, they were quiet. They were silent, the light was silent, but falsely—for beneath these obvious silences other sounds, faint, intractable, began to be heard. Creakings, a groan of wood, a light spatter of moving plaster, from somewhere the trickle of water from a broken pipe. The whole house rustled. A legion of invisible plastermice seemed to be pattering up and down the walls. Little, light sounds, but massing a portentous strength. The house, suddenly stretched by blast, was settling itself. It might settle down on to new and firm purchases, it might be racking itself further, slowly, slowly grinding apart before a sudden collapse. Walking in such houses, the walls and floors are forgotten; the mind pictures only the vivid inner framework of beams and supports, where they might run and how, under stress, they might behave; the house is perceived as a skeleton.

'Down in the courtyard they were carrying a man out from the opposite block. We caught a glance of him through the twisted framework of an iron footbridge. They had laid him on a blanketed stretcher on the grey rubble. He lay still, bloodless, only his face showing, and that plastered with the same sick grey dust. It lay evenly on him, like a poisonous mask—he looked gassed with dust. Once he struggled, his head turned from side to side. He seemed to be trying to speak. It was as if his real face, clean and agonized, tried to be free and show its pain.'

30th June. Aldwych. The bomb fell at about two o'clock on a Friday afternoon. It was the lunch hour and many people were in the street at the time—returning to their offices or visiting the nearby bank and post office. The bomb struck the open at the main door of the Air Ministry building on the north of the wide curving street. Many were instantly killed there on the spot—but fortunately the buildings themselves, of reinforced construction, withstood the shock, thus preventing the disaster, even greater, of mass burial.

The Flying Column despatched straightway to the Aldwych arrived on a scene of terrible slaughter. A light mist lifted to unveil those wide pavements littered with shapes of the dead and wounded. In the canyon of the Aldwych's white masonry they were scattered like the victims of a massacre in some spacious curved arena. And this freshly daylit, terrible scene was further confounded by odd wreckages—the twisted frames of a line of buses parked there, and on the pavement and the road a pathetic snow of currency notes.

The most pressing need was the quick dispersal of so vast a number of casualties: and here chance provided a group of army lorries then in the vicinity. These helped remove the more lightly injured; in all, sixteen ambulances were used, together with many other vehicles. The commercial buildings nearby opened up their First Aid Posts. The dead were shrouded and ranged on the pavement for the mortuary van. Fire Service hoses were used in some places to clean the pavements of blood.

An incident inquiry point manned by the Women's Voluntary Service attended to hundreds of inquiries. With so many casual passers-by involved, the problem of identification was of some proportion. Gradually the position was assessed; and with the casualties removed and the black-out curtains flapping from the black squares of these hundred high windows, the street was slowly cleared. Aldwych, disrupted so suddenly by a moment of winged thunder yet structurally unaltered, reverted to a bruised and shaken normal.

5th July. Westmorland Terrace. This bomb dived straight to earth without cutting out its engine, accelerating thus from over four hundred miles per hour in a savage dive to a spot only twenty yards from the

Peabody Avenue incident of four days previously. Members of a Heavy Rescue Squad working on the original site were trapped. Since it was six o'clock and still daylight a number of people were on the street. These were caught badly; seventy-two casualties were tended, of whom ten were killed. One man, riding a bicycle, was blown into a nearby building, whose gratings and stone slabs at street level were lifted up in the second of explosion to receive the laterally blown bicycle—then subsiding like a closing door into the original position.

An escape of coal gas complicated rescue work in one part of the debris. Once more (though this was not general) military lorries were at hand to help remove the injured. It was the first occasion on which a loudspeaker van was used at a flying-bomb incident to control crowds and give advice to the homeless—who on this occasion numbered very many, involving finally two hundred separate removals of family furniture.

American troops gave most useful assistance at this incident, as at many others. Since there was fair daylight, the major clearance was effected in some four hours. It had been different four nights before, when the Peabody Avenue bomb had fallen in heavy rain at three o'clock in the morning: though in that case casualties were lighter—for surface shelters, crowded through the evacuation of many people from a previous incident in nearby Winchester Street, took the full force of the blast without sustaining damage, proving again the good protection offered by such shelters, which for the first time in the war were becoming thoroughly popular.

It might be noted here that in practically every case in Westminster the first flying-bomb was followed afterwards, perhaps days afterwards, by a second that struck somewhere in the vicinity: this coincidence is notably evident in any map giving the fall positions.

24th July. Hyde Park at the Dell. The bomb fell just after three o'clock in the afternoon. It was a Monday so that the park was not so crowded as it had been on the two week-end days before. But there were a few people about, and two were killed, with twelve others injured. Two men had a remarkable escape: they were found shocked on a bench afterwards—and it transpired that they had been standing only *fifteen yards* from the place where the bomb struck. They had thrown themselves to the ground, and miraculously the blast had hopped over them —though it blew to pieces people farther away.

No widespread disaster was caused by this incident. The bomb fell in the Dell, that declivity of lawn decorated with a pond, a flowered fairy-place where rabbits may be seen to play. Trees were strewn and shrubs uprooted. The memory of these flying-bombs that fell in the park is perfumed with the green smell of sap. Though the tree-trunks themselves withstood with astounding resilience the force of such blast, nevertheless all the summer leaves would be ripped off, scattered and silted on the grass beneath the bark-stripped trunks whose sap now exuded a strong, rich smell, incredibly thick, almost sickening, the odour of green blood.

The defences in Southern England (as security dictated that Kent, Sussex and Surrey should then be called) gradually prevailed in their gallant battle. The weather improved: and fewer bombs reached London. Many were shot down by Spitfires or anti-aircraft fire, some were caught in the vast balloon barrage that could faintly be seen investing the sky to the south in astounding density. Then the army overran the launching sites. London thought itself freed again.

But on 8th September, with no warning, a shattering explosion punctuated the afternoon. It was a curious explosion, a double thunderclap, followed by the noise of a remote and aerial express train. The streets speculated. No warning? No news in the paper? Then perhaps an arms factory explosion? A gasholder? Sabotage on some military road?

But soon the news was leaking out. The first Long-Range Rocket had arrived. It was rumoured that the crater was a quarter mile across, that twenty-five tons of explosive made up the warhead, that a new freezing explosive was being used. Much of this had been hinted at by the German radio. Rocket projectiles were the next most expected development. And a silence on the part of the Press lent wings—or more properly jet-fuel—to the rumour. The word was circulated that secrecy was definitely to be observed, and that it would be as well to regard the explosions as town gas explosions. Hence, for some puzzled and uneasy weeks, Londoners began the wry fable of 'flying gas-mains'.

Secrecy was maintained throughout the period so that every impediment might be placed in the way of German range plotters. In point of fact, most people in Westminster knew within twenty minutes by bush telegraph where the first explosion had taken place. But secrecy was maintained to the extent possible: though soon a general announcement was made that the famous flying gas-mains were in reality rockets despatched from the Hague district of Holland.

Iced-steel fragments were found in the crater of the first rocket, and some conjecture was raised on the question of a freezing explosive having become a truth. However, soon more became known of the weapon, of its speed faster than sound, of its high trajectory that could produce a stratospherical ice formation before descent. By far the greatest worry was the question of its speed—and the problem of warning. This was never properly solved, though observation of condensation trails and launching over the coast of Holland did produce a radioed intelligence of a minute or more. So there began a trying period for the responsible services of Civil Defence. The Wardens' Service had to be ready for instant action throughout the twenty-four hour period, with no relaxation. In place of the spotting system, Posts were made responsible for sending in Vicinity Reports based on the sounds of clattering glass. In addition, since the rockets were not designed to burst on impact as had done the flying-bombs, but instead penetrated deeply, they were thus apt again to dislocate various utility conduits—though in proportion the surface blast area decreased.

Gradually the attack accelerated. And throughout the period, which eventually reached a peak in March, there were also despatched flying-bombs. These were launched both from planes and from longer-range land-sites: they came mostly at night, directed from the east and northeast, and none of them fell in Westminster, though of course the danger was never absent.

In fact, only one other incident occurred within the City limits, the fall of a rocket at Speaker's Corner in Hyde Park near the Marble Arch. This occurred on the 18th March, at nine-thirty in the morning. Three persons in the area were killed, and eighty-one others hurt: though only two were killed and some dozen injured on Westminster territory, the boroughs of Paddington and Marylebone suffering the remainder of this injury. Notwithstanding, the early hour of the rocket's demise averted what would have been a catastrophe of appalling dimension had the explosion taken place in the afternoon—when some thousands of people would have been watching there a march past of the National Fire Service—or, of course, had it occurred at any time when the tub-thumping free speakers were addressing that celebrated corner of casual crowds. As it was, this, the last rocket from the restricted State, fell nearly enough on the kerb of Free Speech. Windows were blown round the Marble Arch, the trees were stripped of their pungent leaves, a water main was broken: but the speech of only a tragic few mouths was closed for ever.

Apart from this one direct hit, there was certain blast felt on the boundaries of the City—the Holborn, Waterloo, Marylebone, Chelsea and City of London boundaries each receiving injury at various times.

Rockets sometimes exploded in the air. On the 12th November one of these exploded over the Victoria area, scattering its fragments all over the City. When this occurred in daylight, there appeared suddenly and silently—as once in a clear blue afternoon sky—a white expanding blossom of smoke like a puff of anti-aircraft fire, only larger; and only some seconds afterwards echoing down to earth its resonant, distant thunderclap of sound. At night a rocket-burst occurring far up, without warning, would paint an abrupt orange moon in the high black sky; again silently, suddenly, arriving and expanding and quickly fading, as though up in the night an evil orange eye had winked at man's frailty.

On the 27th March the last rocket explosion was heard in London: and on the morning at breakfast time the last flying-bomb arrived— after which the launching sites in Holland were overrun. Thereafter London was at peace. After months of sudden explosion, of the thought that at any moment, day or night, in the bath or at the office or at lunch or hanging out the washing, the giant fin-tailed monster might come arrowing down exactly where one stood—after these months of fatalist tension, London was freed.

During the last months, a new neurosis flourished, the anxiety against being killed by 'the last bullet'. Many who had survived the years of danger felt the flutter of their hearts in their mouths when they imagined the last unlucky chance. When people heard of the final shelling of luckless Dover, when they heard on some fine days the resonance of our guns liquidating the last German garrisons in the besieged French channel ports, or when the boom of the rocket suddenly erupted in the London air—many felt anxious and irritated at what seemed a futile killing when the main course of the war was so patently decided.

However, the last casualty from a rocket was not to be suffered till June. Then, in the streets crowded with revellers, the final casualty occurred—a woman injured by a small British rocket misfired in cele- bration of the final Japanese capitulation on the last victory celebration in June.

ENVOI

O n May 6th England knew of the German capitulation. On May 7th there was held the first of the Victory celebrations, a public holiday with much festivity in the streets. So that as dusk fell on this day the watcher from a high tower saw the traffic stopped and the streets of the West End and Whitehall thronged with a slow-moving, quick-cheering crowd of Londoners and visitors gathered to celebrate now the symbolic fact of their real release. Slow-moving, for there were millions there; quick-cheering, for a jubilation was unrestrainable despite the distant pall of action still in the Far East; and groups danced, others sang, they wore their comic hats and their streamers and cheered speakers and drank the pubs dry. The watcher, more silent on his tower, would have then seen to grow with the vanishing day a strange and terrible mirage—for it seemed that in this hour of the end of almost six years there was imposed upon London a mirage of the days of bombardment. London, in a hundred places, was on fire again, the ghost of the Blitz was abroad. . . .

Because, at a hundred corners and squares and on a hundred bombed sites, bonfires had been lit: wood—often the residue of old bombing—had been gathered and set up in open spaces—often the derelict site of a fire from the old days of bombardment. To these the twilight flame had been applied, just as in the siren days, and now pinpointed across the City appeared the first urgent firebursts, evergrowing, as though they were, in fact, spreading, as each bonfire reddened and cast its coppery glow on the house-rows, on glassy windows and the black blind spaces where windows once had been. Alleys lit up, streets took on the fireset glare—it seemed that in each dark declivity of houses there raged again the old fire. The ghosts of wardens and fire-guards and firemen were felt scurrying again down in the redness. Fireworks peppered the air with a parody of gunfire. The smell of burning wood charred the nostrils. And, gruesomely correct, some of the new street lights and fluorescent window lights in different parts glowed fiercely bluish-white, bringing again the shrill memory of the old white thermite glare of the bursting incendiary. A macabre spectacle to the watcher on the tower, silent with his memories, conscious again of the breadth of the great town beneath, and of the scurrying effort of its tiny citizens. But among the citizens—joy, the fireworks of victory, the bonfires and songs of deliverance.

Of what was the mirage, in fact, composed? What, separate from the song, did it relate? The deaths of 1,104, the serious wounding of 2,495, the scratching and shocking—perhaps inerasably—of thousands of others. Thus the casualties—but this negation has its unspoken affirmative, for who can say how many were saved? There is an unknown figure abroad. The sum of the achievement of hard, tedious, dangerous work by thousands of the semi-civilian, semi-scorned civil defenders who, in their moments of action, were startled by the sudden echo of applause. Hundreds of wardens, rescuers, firemen, nurses, doctors, engineers and all the others with their lucubrating office staffs behind them. It is due to their work that so much of the City has been saved, so many lives and limbs salvaged and healed and guarded.

Now, as the memory of the war subsides, as the strategies fall into perspective and the humanities become forgotten—a new phenomenon may be seen, here and there, in the City streets. This takes the form of a man, usually elderly, walking one knows not whither and doing one knows not what, but *dressed* in a dark blue beret and a dark blue over- coat. He is one of quite a few. He was once a warden. As the service was stood down, he relinquished his uniform. Now months afterwards, a nostalgia has set in for times that were not wholly bad. He takes out his uniform, feels the familiar touch, puts it on, and thus walks out on to the street. He is a man who never before would have considered wearing a beret—he is a bowler-hat, a trilby. But now for him the feel of the brimless cap has a meaning, a comfortable grip. It is a reminder of times when, despite the disgusts of death and destruction, there was in his service and among his fellows a good communal tolerance, a gener- osity of spirit, a bone of comradeship that was real and not romantic.

He wears the coat now, he will say, to keep him warm: the beret, because it is comfortable. But that is not the truth. The truth lies in the memory of stripped vanities, of belief in the common purpose, in a shifting of ambition from his self to other people and to all people.

Civil Defence Communications
(Operational)

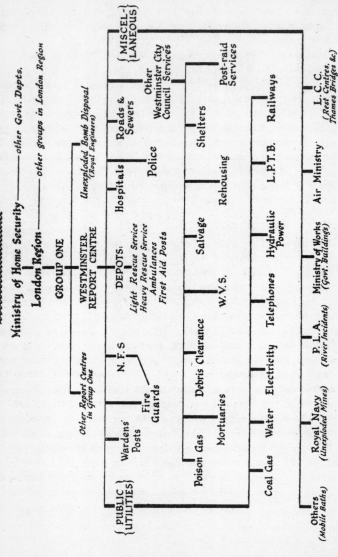

Ministry of Home Security ——— other Govt. Depts.

London Region ——— other groups in London Region

GROUP ONE

Other Report Centres in Group One

WESTMINSTER REPORT CENTRE

Unexploded Bomb Disposal (Royal Engineers)

{ PUBLIC UTILITIES }

Wardens' Posts

N.F.S

Fire Guards

DEPOTS:
Light Rescue Service
Heavy Rescue Service
Ambulances
First Aid Posts

Hospitals

Police

Roads & Sewers

Other Westminster City Council Services

{ MISCEL- LANEOUS }

Post-raid Services

Poison Gas

Mortuaries

Debris Clearance

W.V.S.

Salvage

Rehousing

Shelters

Coal Gas

Water

Electricity

Telephones

Hydraulic Power

L.P.T.B.

Railways

Others
(Mobile Baths)

Royal Navy
(Unexploded Mines)

P.L.A.
(River Incidents)

Ministry of Works
(Govt. Buildings)

Air Ministry

L.C.C.
(Rest Centres, Thames Bridges &c.)

APPENDIX

William Sansom first made his reputation with a collection of stories, Fireman Flower *(1944), which drew on his wartime experiences as a London fireman. Reprinted below is 'The Wall', one of the most powerful stories from that collection.*

THE WALL

It was our third job that night.

Until this thing happened, work had been without incident. There had been shrapnel, a few enquiring bombs, and some huge fires; but these were unremarkable and have since merged without indentity into the neutral maze of fire and noise and water and night, without date and without hour, with neither time nor form, that lowers mistily at the back of my mind as a picture of the air-raid season.

I suppose we were worn down and shivering. Three a.m. is a meanspirited hour. I suppose we were drenched, with the cold hose water trickling in at our collars and settling down at the tails of our shirts. Without doubt the heavy brass couplings felt moulded from metal-ice. Probably the open roar of the pumps drowned the petulant buzz of the raiders above, and certainly the ubiquitous fire-glow made an orange stage-set of the streets. Black water would have puddled the City alleys and I suppose our hands and our faces were black as the water. Black with hacking about among the burnt up rafters. These things were an every-night nonentity. They happened and they were not forgotten because they were never even remembered.

But I do remember it was our third job. And there we were—Len, Lofty, Verno and myself, playing a fifty foot jet up the face of a tall city warehouse and thinking of nothing at all. You don't think of anything after the first few hours. You just watch the white pole of water lose itself in the fire and you think of nothing. Sometimes you move the jet over to another window. Sometimes the orange dims to black—but you only ease your grip on the ice-cold nozzle and continue pouring careless gallons through the window. You know the fire will fester for hours yet. However, that night the blank, indefinite hours of waiting were sharply interrupted—by an unusual sound. Very suddenly a long rattling crack of bursting brick and mortar perforated the moment. And then the upper half of that five-storey building heaved over towards us. It hung

203

there, poised for a timeless second before rumbling down at us. I was thinking of nothing at all and then I was thinking of everything in the world.

In that simple second my brain digested every detail of the scene. New eyes opened at the sides of my head so that, from within, I photographed a hemispherical panorama bounded by the huge length of the building in front of me and the narrow lane on either side.

Blocking us on the left was the squat trailer pump, roaring and quivering with effort. Water throbbed from its overflow valves and from leakages in the hose and couplings. A ceaseless stream spewed down its grey sides into the gutter. But nevertheless a fat iron exhaust pipe glowed red-hot in the middle of the wet engine. I had to look past Lofty's face. Lofty was staring at the controls, hands tucked into his armpits for warmth. Lofty was thinking of nothing. He had a black diamond of soot over one eye, like the White-eyed Kaffir in negative.

To the other side of me was a free run up the alley. Overhead swung a sign—"Catto and Henley." I wondered what in hell they sold. Old stamps? The alley was quite free. A couple of lengths of dead, deflated hose wound over the darkly glistening pavement. Charred flotsam dammed up one of the gutters. A needle of water fountained from a hole in a live hose-length. Beneath a blue shelter light lay a shattered coping stone. The next shop along was a tobacconist's, windowless, with fake display cartons torn open for anybody to see. The alley was quite free.

Behind me, Len and Verno shared the weight of the hose. They heaved up against the strong backward drag of waterpressure. All I had to do was yell "Drop it"—and then run. We could risk the live hose snaking up at us. We could run to the right down the free alley—Len, Verno and me. But I never moved. I never said "Drop it" or anything else. That long second held me hypnotized, rubber boots cemented to the pavement. Ton upon ton of red-hot brick hovering in the air above us numbed all initiative. I could only think. I couldn't move.

Six yards in front stood the blazing building. A minute before I would never have distinguished it from any other drab Victorian atrocity happily on fire. Now I was immediately certain of every minute detail. The building was five storeys high. The top four storeys were fiercely alight. The rooms inside were alive with red fire. The black outside walls remained untouched. And thus, like the lighted carriages of a night express, there appeared alternating rectangles of black and red that emphasized vividly the extreme symmetry of the window spacing: each oblong window shape posed as a vermilion panel set in perfect order upon the dark face of the wall. There were ten windows to each floor, making forty windows in all. In rigid rows of ten, one row placed precisely above the other, with strong contrasts of black and red, the blazing windows stood to attention in strict formation. The oblong

THE WALL

building, the oblong windows, the oblong spacing. Orange-red colour seemed to *bulge* from the black frame-work, assumed tactile values, like boiling jelly that expanded inside a thick black squared grill.

Three of the storeys, thirty blazing windows and their huge frame of black brick, a hundred solid tons of hard, deep Victorian wall, pivoted over towards us and hung flatly over the alley. Whether the descending wall actually paused in its fall I can never know. Probably it never did. Probably it only seemed to hang there. Probably my eyes digested its action at an early period of momentum, so that I saw it "off true" but before it had gathered speed.

The night grew darker as the great mass hung over us. Through smoke-fogged fireglow the moonlight had hitherto penetrated to the pit of our alley through declivities in the skyline. Now some of the moonlight was being shut out as the wall hung ever further over us. The wall shaded the moonlight like an inverted awning. Now the pathway of light above had been squeezed to a thin line. That was the only silver lining I ever believed in. It shone out—a ray of hope. But it was a declining hope, for although at this time the entire hemispherical scene appeared static, an imminence of movement could be sensed throughout—presumably because the scene was actually moving. Even the speed of the shutter which closed the photograph on my mind was powerless to exclude this motion from a deeper consciousness. The picture appeared static to the limited surface senses, the eyes and the material brain, but beyond that there was hidden movement.

The second was timeless. I had leisure to remark many things. For instance, that an iron derrick, slightly to the left, would not hit me. This derrick stuck out from the building and I could feel its sharpness and hardness as clearly as if I had run my body intimately over its contour. I had time to notice that it carried a footlong hook, a chain with three-inch rings, two girder supports and a wheel more than twice as large as my head.

A wall will fall in many ways. It may sway over to the one side or the other. It may crumble at the very beginning of its fall. It may remain intact and fall flat. This wall fell as flat as a pancake. It clung to its shape through ninety degrees to the horizontal. Then it detached itself from the pivot and slammed down on top of us.

The last resistance of bricks and mortar at the pivot point cracked off like automatic gun fire. The violent sound both deafened us and brought us to our senses. We dropped the hose and crouched. Afterwards Verno said that I knelt slowly on one knee with bowed head, like a man about to be knighted. Well, I got my knighting. There was an incredible noise—a thunderclap condensed into the space of an eardrum—and then the bricks and the mortar came tearing and burning into the flesh of my face.

THE WALL

Lofty, away by the pump, was killed. Len, Verno and myself they dug out. There was very little brick on top of us. We had been lucky. We had been framed by one of those symmetrical, oblong window spaces.

INDEX

INDEX

INDEX

INDEX

INDEX

Water supplies, maintenance of, 150, 151, 152, 153–4, 155

Waterloo Bridges, hit, 81

Waverton Street, incident in, 97

Weather, and bombs, 14–5

Wednesday, the (April 16th), raid on, 75 *et seq.*

Wellington Arch, 55, 193

Wellington Barracks, 43, 67, 128; hit, 81, 186–7, 192

West End, 9, 15–6, 31; incidents in, 25, 37–8, 63–4 (*see also districts*); and raids on Buckingham Palace, 40–1

Westminster Abbey, 17, 35, 44; and precincts, damage to, 48, 63, 82, 85 *et seq.*

Westminster, City of, extent of, 9; Council, 10–1, 13; districts of, 14 *et seq.*; only civic funeral, 69, 144; number of incidents and casualties during Blitz, 92–4; type of buildings, 113, 114, 122, 134; during Pilotless Blitz, 187–8

Westminster Hospital, 17

Westminster Pier, 160

Westminster School, damage to, 85, 87–8; Fire Station at, 121

Westminster Training College, hit, 183

Westmorland Avenue, incident in, 193

Westmorland Terrace, incident described, 195–6

Wheelbarrow rescue technique, 71

Whitehall, 9, 17, 18, 29, 31, 37, 84; A.R.P. in, 16, 108; incidents in, 34, 44, 45, 48, 55, 56, 58, 62–3, 82, 180

Whitehall Theatre, 18

Whitehall Place, No. 5, hit, 55, 56

Wild Street, incident in, 192

Wilfred Street, incident in, 192

Willesden, 27

Winchester Street, incident in, 193

Windmill Theatre, 63

Women's Voluntary Service, work of, 104, 110, 127–8, 141